Issued under the authority of the

Manual of
Firemanship

A survey of the science of fire-fighting

Book 9
Fire protection
of buildings

London
HMSO

First published 1977
Second edition 1990
The previous publishing history of
this volume is shown on pages 204–207

ISBN 0 11 340989 3

Preface

The protection of buildings against fire is a constantly developing science. The design of new buildings, their contents and the materials used present ever-changing problems to the designers and manufacturers of automatic fire detection equipment and fixed extinguishing installations, not to mention fire prevention officers. High-bay warehouses, shopping precincts, atria, computer suites etc. all require very different approaches and solutions.

This Book explains the main principles governing installations and illustrates them by examples. Students, however, should constantly update their knowledge by reading appropriate publications and, where possible, inspecting actual installations.

References in this Book to the male person should be construed as applying, where appropriate, to the female person also. The qualifications of appointment to and promotion within the Fire Service (Appointments and Promotion) Regulations 1965 applied only to men. By virtue of the Fire Service (Appointments and Promotion) (Amendment) Regulations 1976 they now apply equally to women. Reference to firemen and other male holders of Fire Service rank should therefore be interpreted as references to firewomen and female holders of such rank also.

The Home Office is indebted to all who have helped in the preparation of this work.

Home Office
1990

Metrication

List of SI units for use in the Fire Service

Quantity and basic or derived SI unit and symbol	Approved unit of measurement	Conversion factor
Length metre (m)	kilometer (km) metre (m) millimetre (mm)	1 km = 0.621 mile 1 m = 1.093 yards = 3.279 feet 1 mm = 0.039 inch
Area square metre (m^2)	square kilometre (km^2) square metre (m^2) square millimetre (mm^2)	1 km^2 = 0.386 $mile^2$ 1 m^2 = 1.196 $yards^2$ = 10.764 $feet^2$ 1 mm^2 = 0.002 $inch^2$
Volume cubic metre (m^3)	cubic metre (m^3) litre (l) ($=10^{-3}m^3$)	1 m^3 = 35.7 $feet^3$ 1 litre = 0.22 gallon
Volume, flow cubic metre per second (m^3/s)	cubic metre per second (m^3/s) litres per minute (l/min)	1 m^3/s = 35.7 $feet^3/s$ 1l/min = 0.22 gall/min
Mass kilogram (kg)	kilogram (kg) tonne (t)	1 kg = 2.205 lbs 1 t = 0.984 ton
Velocity metre per second (m/s)	metre per second (m/s) international knot (kn) (= 1.852km/h) kilometre per hour (km/h)	1 m/s = 3.281 feet/second 1 km/h = 0.621 mile/hour
Acceleration metre per $second^2$ (m/s^2)	metre/$second^2$ (m/s^2)	1 m/s^2 = 3.281 feet/$second^2$ = 0.102 'g'
Force newton (N)	kilonewton (kN) newton (n)	1 kN = 0.1 ton force 1 N = 0.225 lb force

Quantity and basic or derived SI unit and symbol	Approved unit of measurement	Conversion factor
Energy, work joule (J) (= 1 Nm)	joule (J) Kilojoule (kJ) Kilowatt/hour (kW/h)	1 kJ = 0.953 British Thermal Unit 1 J = 0.738 foot lb force
Power watt (W) (= 1 J/s = 1 Nm/s)	kilowatt (kW) watt (W)	1 kW = 1.34 horsepower 1 W = 0.735 foot lb force/second
Pressure newton/metre^2(N/m^2)	bar (=10^{5}N/m^2) millibar (mbar) (=10^{2}N/m^2) metrehead (=0.0981 bar)	1 bar = 0.991 atmosphere = 14.5 lb force/in^2 1 mbar = 0.0288 inch Hg 1 metrehead = 3.28 foot head
Heat, quantity of heat joule (J)	joule (J) kilojoule (kJ)	1 kJ = 0.953 British Thermal Unit
Heat flow rate watt	watt (W) kilowatt (kW)	1 W = 3.41 British Thermal Units/hour 1 kW = 0.953 British Thermal Unit/Second
Specific energy, calorific value, specific latent heat joule/kilogram (J/kg) joule/m^3 (J/m^3)	kilojoule/kilogram (kJ/kg) kilojoule/m^3 (kJ/m^3) megajoule/m^3 (mJ/m^3)	1 kJ/kg = 0.43 British Thermal Unit/lb 1 kJ/m^3 = 0.0268 British Thermal Unit/ft^3
Temperature degree Celsius (°C)	degree Celsius (°C)	1 degree Celsius = 1 degree Centigrade

Contents

Part 1
Fire extinguishing systems

Part 2
Fire alarm systems

Part 3
Fire venting systems

Chapter 21 Ventilation in multi-storey buildings

Chapter 22 Pressurisation

List of plates

17 Entrance to a shopping mall. All the perimeter windows are vertical casement automatic ventilators.
Photo: Colt International Ltd

18 Louvred fire and smoke automatic ventilators fitted into a typical long mall.
Photo: Colt International Ltd

19 Similar louvred ventilators, to those in Plate 18, fitted to a flat roof.
Photo: Colt International Ltd

20 Powered heat and smoke ventilators either manually or automatically controlled.
Photo: Colt International Ltd

21 Part of shopping mall with smoke curtains/dams retracted.
Photo: Colt International Ltd

22 As Plate 21 with curtains/dams operated.
Photo: Colt International Ltd

23 Another example of a shopping mall showing vertical and roof ventilators.
Photo: Colt International Ltd

24 Typical metal ducting being fitted into a shopping mall.
Photo: Capital and Counties Ltd

Part 1
Fire extinguishing systems

Fixed systems of pipework using only water as the extinguishing medium have proved efficient in the protection of buildings, and many other classes of risk, against extensive damage resulting from outbreaks of fire. Such systems can be divided into three main classes – automatic sprinklers, drenchers and water spray projector systems.

Automatic sprinklers are installed inside a building and operate when a fire occurs. Drenchers, which can be automatically or manually operated, are fitted outside a building in order to protect it from a fire in nearby property. Water spray systems are automatic and specially designed for extinguishing fires involving oils or flammable liquids

Automatic sprinklers are dealt with in Chapters 1–6, other installations using water in Chapter 8. Chapter 9 describes installations not using water e.g. CO_2, vaporising liquids and powder. These are designed for the protection of risks for which water is unsuitable as an extinguishing medium.

Special systems are sometimes designed for a specific risk and are, usually, highly sophisticated and two examples are described in Chapter 7.

Chapter 1
Automatic sprinklers:
principles of design

1 General

Since a most important principle of successful fire extinction is to attack an outbreak immediately, it follows that any device which can detect a fire automatically and then control or extinguish it with the minimum loss, must be of great value. Automatic sprinkler systems using water as the extinguishing medium have been universally adopted as one means of achieving this purpose.

Basically an automatic sprinkler installation comprises of a system of pipes erected at, or near, the ceiling on each floor of a building and connected, through controlling valves, to one or more water supplies. At intervals on the pipework are sealed outlets called sprinkler heads. These incorporate a device whereby a rise in temperature to a predetermined limit causes the sprinkler to open and water to be discharged in the form of a spray over an area of the floor below. The sprinklers are so spaced that the spray from any two sprinklers overlap leaving no part of the floor unprotected.

The operation of the sprinkler leads to the opening of a valve which causes an alarm bell to ring. The layout of a typical sprinkler system is shown in Fig. 1.1.

2 Historical

The first automatic sprinklers were invented in the mid-19th century. Various types were produced, one of the most successful by Grinnell in 1882. This incorporated a fusible soldered link which melted when heated and released water through the sprinkler head. From this design many modern solder-type heads have been developed.

Shortly after the first World War, two major developments took place: the introduction of the glass bulb sprinkler head and the multiple control system. These are described in Chapters 5 and 6 respectively.

Efforts have been made to perfect a system by which the water would be automatically turned off when the fire had been extinguished. One such system has been developed called the 're-cycling pre-action system' (see page 28).

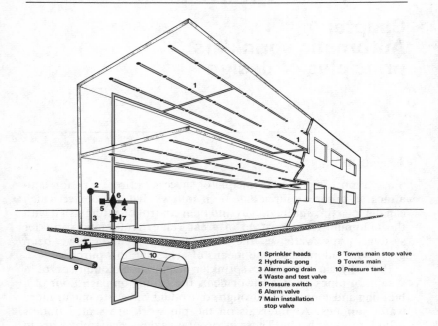

1 Sprinkler heads   8 Towns main stop valve
2 Hydraulic gong   9 Towns main
3 Alarm gong drain   10 Pressure tank
4 Waste and test valve
5 Pressure switch
6 Alarm valve
7 Main installation
   stop valve

Fig. 1.1 Layout of a typical sprinkler system

3   Installation and design requirements

At the time of publication, there is no national legislation compell-
ing owners of property to install a sprinkler system in a building.
Under local legislation in some areas, plans of certain types of
building will only receive approval if adequate provision for
sprinklers is made. Insurance companies encourage the installation
of sprinkler systems by giving substantial reductions in premiums
for property so protected. They, through the Loss Prevention
Council (LPC), lay down the minimum standards necessary.

Sprinkler systems are designed in accordance with

(i)   British Standard 5306 Pt.2

(ii)   LPC rules for Automatic Sprinkler Installations

These two documents have recently become synonymous and any
amendment to one is now reflected in the other. Further reference
in the Manual will be to 'the BS/LPC Rules'.

A new addition to the BS/LCP Rules is with regard to the use of
sprinkler systems for protection of life e.g. in shopping centres. This
area of specification will be expanded in further revisions of the
rules.

Systems are now tailor made to suit the particular occupancy and are designed to produce a certain density of water spray over a pre-determined area for a given period of time depending on the expected area of fire development in that particular occupancy (see Section 6).

Sprinkler installations are used to protect a very wide range of premises and there are very few buildings which are totally unsuitable for sprinklers. Where parts of a building contain materials or processes for which water would be unsuitable as an extinguishing medium, these areas can be isolated by fire resisting construction and the remainder protected by sprinklers.

At the present time (1989) there are tentative proposals to fit sprinklers, of a fast-response type (see Chapter 5 Section 4), in private houses and experiments are being carried out.

The terms (a) 'high rise' and (b) 'low rise' systems are used to describe systems where;

(a) the highest sprinkler is more than 45m above ground level or the sprinkler pumps, and,

(b) the highest sprinkler is not more than 45m above ground or the sprinkler pump.

4   Risk categories

The BS/LPC arranges occupancies into risk categories each having an accepted abbreviation. These are shown in Table 1

Table 1
BS/LPC risk categories

Category	Abbreviation
Light hazard	LH
Ordinary hazard: Group 1	OH1
Ordinary hazard: Group 2	OH2
Ordinary hazard: Group 3	OH3
Ordinary hazard: Group 3 Special	OH3(S)
High hazard	HH

a. Light hazard (LH)
These are premises containing hazards of the non-industrial type e.g. offices, libraries where the amount and combustibility of the contents is low.

b. Ordinary hazards: OH1, OH2, OH3, OH3(S)

Ordinary hazards are commercial and industrial premises involving the handling, processing and storage of a very wide range of mainly combustible materials which are unlikely to burn intensely in the early stages of a fire. It has been found necessary to sub-divide them into four groups as below.

OH1   breweries, dairies and restaurants

OH2   engineering works, garages, medium size retail shops

OH3   soap factories, sugar refineries, aircraft factories

OH3 (S) film and television studios, cotton mills, match factories

c. High hazard (HH)

This category covers commercial and industrial occupancies having abnormal fire loads:

(i)   where materials handled or processed are mainly of an extra hazardous nature likely to develop rapid and intensely-burning fires;

(ii)   involving high-piled storage;
According to the hazardous nature of the stock and the height of the storage, those included in section (ii) are sub-divided into four categories:

Category I   Process high hazards
Category II   High-piled storage hazards
Category III   Potable spirit storage hazards
Category IV   Oil and flammable liquids hazards

The term 'storage' includes the warehousing or temporary depositing of goods or materials.

5   Classes of system

Three classes of sprinkler system have been developed to suit the above risk categories and are called:

(a) light hazard system

(b) ordinary hazard system

(c) high hazard system

Pipework for two or more different types of hazard system may be connected to a common set of control valves provided the total number of sprinklers does not exceed the permitted maximum. Each of these systems is designed to give the appropriate density of discharge over an assumed area of maximum operation (AAMO) in the highest and most hydraulically-remote parts of a protected building.

6 Design density and assumed area of maximum operation

The amount of water required to control or extinguish a fire is called the minimum design density and will depend, among other criteria, on the type of hazard involved. Minimum design density is pre-set according to the recommendations of BS/LPC Rules and is specified for each hazard class. The standard requires that the minimum design density of discharge of water in mm/min from a particular group of sprinklers be not less than a given value (see Table 2). This group of sprinklers – usually numbering four or more – is that which is most hydraulically remote from the water supply and constitutes part of a 'larger group' of sprinklers discharging simultaneously.

The 'larger group' forms the 'area of assumed maximum operation' (AAMO). This is the maximum area over which it is assumed, for design purposes, sprinklers will operate in a fire. The hydraulically most removed AAMO is used to calculate design density.

Table 2

Minimum design density and AAMO for light, ordinary and high hazard (process) roof or ceiling sprinklers

Hazard	Minimum design density	AAMO
Light	mm/min	m²
	2.25	84
Ordinary		
Group I	5	72
Group II	5	144
Group III	5	216
Group III special	5	360
High (process)		
Type 1	7.5	260
Type 2	10.0	260
Type 3	12.5	260
Type 4	10.0	complete deluge protection for each building

7 Life safety systems

a. General

The use of sprinkler installations in the saving of lives by preventing the development of fire is well understood. As a result, in the last two decades sprinkler systems have played an increasing role in life safety fire precautions.

Classification of fire hazards in the current BS/LPC rules considers systems which, additionally, serve for the protection of life, e.g. in closed shopping centres where they are designed to prevent fire spread from shops to adjacent exit routes. Additional safeguards under BS 5588 Pt 10 are also currently under discussion.

b. Requirements

The 'Life Safety' requirements could include the following:–

(i)   The system should be of a wet type.

(ii)   The system should be zoned, each zone being controlled by a separate stop valve and having a maximum of 200 heads.

(iii)   A zone may require the installation control valve-set to be duplicated.

(iv)   No zone shall extend to an area of the building under separate ownership or tenancy.

(v)   No zone shall extend to more than one floor level but a zone may include a mezzanine floor of not more $100m^2$.

(vi)   Stop valves shall be accessible at the floor level of the zone they control.

(vii)   Only one zone of a multi-zone installation shall be shut down at any one time. The fire authority is to be advised of the intention and should have to approve.

(viiii) All stop valves and alarm valves shall be monitored by tamper-proof electrical switches indicating that the valves are in the correct operating mode.

(ix)   All practical steps shall be taken to ensure continuity and reliability of water supplies.

(x)   Means shall be provided to initiate visual and audible warnings to an area with responsible manning when the pressure in the sprinkler trunk falls to the point at which the pump should start. These warnings shall 'latch in' and only be capable of manual cancellation.

(xi)   On indicator panels, audible alarms may be silenced after the system has operated, but the visual alarm signal shall remain until the installation has been reset to its normal operational position.

In theatres and similar buildings, where a fire break curtain is protected by open drenchers or sprinklers, operated by a quick opening valve, the water supply to these should not be taken from that supplying the automatic sprinkler installation.

Chapter 2
Automatic sprinklers: water supplies

General

Automatic sprinkler systems must be provided with a suitable and acceptable water supply. It must have a pressure and flow characteristic not less than that specified in the BS/LPC Rules. It must be automatic, throughly reliable and not subject to either frost or drought conditions that could seriously affect the supply. The supply should be under the control of the occupier of the building containing the installation or, where this is not practicable, the right of use of the supply must be suitably guaranteed.

The water must be free from any matter in suspension which would be liable to cause accumulation in the system pipework. The use of salt or brackish water is not normally allowed. In special circumstances, where there is no suitable fresh water source available, consideration may be given to the use of salt or brackish water provided that the installation is normally charged with fresh water.

1   Types of water supply

Water supplies are graded into three categories:
a. single; b. superior and c. duplicate.

a.   Single supply

These must be either:

(i)   A town main capable of supplying the necessary pressure and flow requirements

(ii)   An automatic booster pump drawing water from the town main capable of supplying the necessary pressure and flow requirements.

(iii)   An automatic suction pump drawing water either from a suction tank complying with BS/LPC Rules or a virtually inexhaustible source i.e. river, lake, canal.

(iv)   Pressure tank supplying water for only one sprinkler system.

b. Superior supply

These will vary according to whether the system is a 'low' or 'high' rise and the occupancy hazard rating.

Low rise systems – a superior supply shall be:

(i)   A town main or

(ii)   Two automatic suction pumps or

(iii)   Two automatic booster pumps or

(iv)   An elevated private reservoir or

(v)   A gravity tank or

for LH or OHl occupancies only:

(vi)   A pressure tank.

High rise systems – a superior supply shall be:

(i)   A gravity tank or

(ii)   An automatic suction pump arrangement in which each installation is served by either a separate pump or separate stage of a multi-stage pump.

c. Duplicate supply

A duplicate supply shall include at least one of the suitable combinations given in Table 3 with the supply pipes from each source joined into a common trunk main as close as possible to the protected premises.

This common trunk main shall not

(i)   traverse ground not under the control of the user or

(ii)   be under a public roadway.

2   Details of particular supplies

a. Town mains

The mains water supply must be fed from both ends by mains, each of which must be capable of sustaining the required pressure and flow. The main at each end must not directly be dependent on a common trunk main in the town main system, and this must be fed from more than one source. The main must be capable of furnishing, at all times of the day and night, the minimum pressure and flow requirements for the appropriate category of risk.

Duplicated connections from the main must be carried separately to the premises, which contain the sprinkler installation, and there should be a stop valve on the main between the two branches. If it is not possible to provide duplicate connections, special consideration may be given to the waiving of the requirement if there is a stop valve (secured open) on the town main immediately on each side of a single branch connection.

In the event of a fracture or partial breakdown of the main, operation of the stop valves ensures that the supply is maintained by that part of the main which is still functioning.

Table 3
Combinations suitable for duplicate supplies

	TOWN MAIN WITH OR WITHOUT BOOSTER PUMP	BOOSTER PUMP FROM ELEVATED PRIVATE RESERVOIR	SUCTION PUMP	GRAVITY TANK	ELEVATED PRIVATE	PRESSURE TANK
PRESSURE TANK	LIGHT ORDINARY	LIGHT ORDINARY	LIGHT ORDINARY	SUITABLE ONLY WITH A THIRD SUPPLY GIVEN AS SUITABLE	LIGHT ORDINARY	SUITABLE ONLY WITH A THIRD SUPPLY GIVEN AS SUITABLE
ELEVATED PRIVATE RESERVOIR	NOT SUITABLE	LIGHT ORDINARY HIGH	LIGHT ORDINARY HIGH	LIGHT ORDINARY HIGH	LIGHT ORDINARY HIGH	
GRAVITY TANK	NOT SUITABLE	LIGHT ORDINARY HIGH	LIGHT ORDINARY HIGH	LIGHT ORDINARY HIGH #		
SUCTION PUMP	NOT USUALLY PERMITTED	LIGHT ORDINARY HIGH	LIGHT ORDINARY HIGH*			
BOOSTER PUMP FROM ELEVATED PRIVATE RESERVOIR	NOT USUALLY PERMITTED	LIGHT ORDINARY HIGH				
TOWN MAIN WITH OR WITHOUT BOOSTER PUMP	LIGHT ORDINARY HIGH					

* A SINGLE VIRTUALLY UNLIMITED SOURCE SUCH AS A LAKE, RIVER OR CANAL MAY BE USED FOR LIGHT HAZARD ONLY

#A DIVIDED TANK MAY BE USED

b. Suction and booster pumps

If a water supply is available with no head or only under limited pressure, a pump may be used to feed water into the installation at the required pressure. In such cases, it is stipulated that the pumps providing a superior supply shall draw water from either: a suction tank with full holding capacity equal to that required for the particular hazard class, or a secondary suction tank of smaller capacity with automatic inflow, provided it meets with BS/LPC requirements.

The most important provisions relating to automatic pumps are as follow:–

(i)   With an automatic pump supply consisting of two automatic pumps, at least one may be driven by a compression ignition (diesel) engine with each pump capable of providing the necessary pressure and flow. With three automatic pumps at least two must have a compression ignition drive. Any two pumps together must be capable of providing the necessary pressure and flow independently. In both arrangements they must be capable of operating in parallel, i.e. with similar pressure and flow characteristics.

(ii)   The pump must be housed in a readily accessible position in a sprinkler-protected building, or in the case of an electric motor-driven pump, it must be housed in a separate building of non-combustible construction used for no other purpose. It must be adequately protected against mechanical damage. The temperature of the room should be maintained above 4°C (10°C where compression ignition engines are used).

(iii)   Automatic priming equipment must be provided where necessary to ensure that the pump will be fully primed with water at all times.

(iv)   The performance characteristics of the pumps should be such that the pressure falls progressively with the rate of demand. They must be capable of providing the rate of flow and pressure required at the highest and most remote parts of the protected premises. The output must be so controlled that there is not an excessive rate of discharge at the lowest level in areas close to the installation valves. To meet these conditions pumps must have performance characteristics complying with the requirements laid down.

(v)   Where permitted by the water authority, a pump may draw directly from a town main, provided the latter is capable of supplying water at all times at the maximum rated output of the pump.

(vi)   The pump should be fully operational within 30 seconds after starting.

(vii)   The pump should have a direct drive and must start automatically. Means should be provided for manual starting and once started the pump must run continuously until stopped manually.

(viii)   Where an automatic pump forms the sole supply, a fall in water pressure in the sprinkler system, which is intended to initiate the automatic starting of the pump, shall at the same time provide a visual and audible alarm at some suitable installation, e.g. in the gatehouse or by the installation control valves.

(ix)   A test for automatic starting of the pump must be carried out weekly.

13

(x) Pumps must be driven either by an electrical motor or an approved compression ignition type of engine. The electric supply must be obtained from a reliable source, preferably from a public supply. Where a compression engine is used, provision must be made for two separate methods of engine starting.

(xi) Any switches to the electric power feed to motors must be clearly labelled: 'Sprinkler pump motor supply – not to be switched off in the event of fire'.

c. Elevated private reservoir – minimum supply capacity

This is defined as similar to a ground reservoir but situated at a higher level than the premises to be protected. Certain conditions regarding capacity must be complied with before this type of reservoir can be used as a source of supply to a sprinkler installation. the minimum capacity ranges from $9m^3$ to $875m^3$ depending on the class of system installed; this is on the understanding that the stored water is used entirely for the sprinkler system.

Where such reservoirs serve other than sprinkler installations, e.g. water for trade and domestic purposes, there must be a constant capacity of at least:–

$500m^3$ in LH categories
$1000m^3$ in OH categories
$1060m^3$ plus the stored capacity 225 to $875m^3$ in HH categories

In certain cases smaller capacities may be accepted but only with the express approval of the LPC.

d. Gravity tank

A gravity tank is defined as a purpose built container. It is erected on the site of the protected premises at such a height as to provide the requisite pressure and flow condition at the installation valves. The tank must be adequately protected against freezing and, where it is not enclosed within a tower, the top must be covered so as to exclude daylight and solid matter.

The main provisions are:–

(i) The tank must have a minimum capacity of $9m^3$ for the light hazard class rising to $875m^3$ for the high hazard. Should the capacity of the tank exceed these requirements, it is permissible to draw upon the surplus for other purposes by means of a side-outlet pipe which must be positioned above the level of the quantity to be reserved for the sprinkler installation.

(ii) The quantity of the water required for the sprinkler installation must be automatically maintained. If the tank forms part of the sole supply to the system, the supply to the tank must be capable of refilling it to the required capacity within six hours.

(iii) The use of one tank to supply installations in two or more buildings under separate ownership is not allowed.

(iv) The tank must be fitted with a depth indicator, a permanent ladder or stairway to permit access and the water must be kept clean and free from sediment.

e. Pressure tanks

A pressure tank is a cylindrical steel vessel with convex ends containing water under pressure.

The pressure tank is an acceptable superior water supply for LH and OH1 categories only, provided:

(1) The water capacity is not less than:
Sole supply: $7m^3$ for LH; $23m^3$ for OH1
Duplicate supply: $7m^3$ for LH; $15m^3$ for OH1 – all groups

(2) There is an approved arrangement for maintaining automatically the required air-pressure and water level into the tank under non-fire conditions.

The general requirements for a pressure tank are:–

(i) It must be housed in a readily acceptable position in a sprinkler protected building of incombustible construction used for no other purpose. The tank must be adequately protected against mechanical damage. The temperature of the room should be maintained above 4°C.

(ii) When used as a single water supply, the tank must be provided with an approved arrangement for maintaining automatically the required air-pressure and water level in the tank under non-fire conditions. The arrangement should include an approved warning system to indicate failure of the devices to restore the correct pressure and water level. This arrangement is also advocated in cases where the tank provides the duplicate supply.

(iii) The tank must be fitted with air pressure gauges and a gauge glass to show the level of the water. Stop valves and back pressure valves must be provided on both the water and air supply connections to the tank and they must be fitted as close to the tank as possible (Fig 2.1).

(iv) Where a pressure tank forms the sole supply to the installation, connections are not allowed to be taken from the

15

supply for any purpose other than sprinklers. If it forms one source of duplicate supply, a pipe not exceeding 50mm may be taken from the combined water supply main to supply hydraulic hose reels for firefighting purposes only, subject to the pressure being replenished automatically as in (ii) above.

The maximum standing air pressure for pressure tanks is 10 bar.

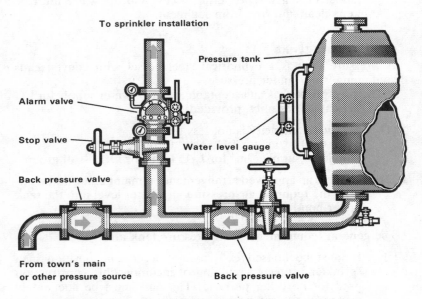

To sprinkler installation

Pressure tank

Alarm valve

Stop valve

Water level gauge

Back pressure valve

From town's main or other pressure source

Back pressure valve

Fig. 2.1 Pressure tank and town main with back pressure valves.

3 Pressure and flow requirements

The BS/LPC Rules lay down the minimum requirements for pressure and flow in any particular sprinkler system. These will vary with the risk category.

a. LH and OH classes

For LH and OH classes, the required pressure at the installation control valve is made up of;

(i)   a nominal pressure figure for a given rate of flow (see Table 4 below) PLUS

(ii) a calculated pressure figure (based on the difference in height between the highest sprinkler and the valve).

16

Table 4

Risk Category	Rate of Flow (L/min)	Nominal Pressure (minimum required running pressure) (Bar)
Light Hazard	225	2.2
Ordinary Hazard (OH1)	375	1.0
	540	0.7
Ordinary Hazard (OH2)	725	1.4
	1000	1.0
Ordinary Hazard (OH3)	1100	1.7
	1350	1.4
Ordinary Hazard (OH3(s))	1800	2.0
	2100	1.5

b.   HH class

In the first case of HH class, specific tables of figures are laid down by the BS/LPC Rules. The point of these tables is to ensure that the water supply is capable of providing the required flow and pressure at the level of the highest sprinkler in the HH portion of the premises. The supply must meet the necessary density of discharge and AAMO specified for that particular class of occupancy.

4   Proving of water supplies

In the case of town mains, elevated private reservoirs and gravity tanks, facilities must be provided to enable proving tests to be carried out at the valves on each installation to verify that the water supply satisfies the requirements of pressure and flow specified for each hazard class. Water supplies from automatic pumps and pressure tanks are designed to meet the pressure and flow conditions appropriate to the hazard class and accordingly it is not necessary to require practical flow tests in these instances.

5   Fire brigade inlets

Sprinkler installations fed solely from water supplies of limited capacity such as a pressure tank, gravity tank or pump suction tank, must be fitted with a fire brigade inlet connection. This is to enable the brigade to pump water into the installation by using their own equipment. The fitting of such inlets to other installations is a strong recommendation to ensure protection under practically all circumstances.

Chapter 3
Automatic sprinklers: protection systems

According to BS/LPC Rules a sprinkler installation should be based on one of the following main types:

(1) Wet pipe system

(2) Dry pipe

(3) Alternate (wet and dry pipe)

(4) Pre-action

(5) Re-cycling pre-action

Systems based on (1) and/or (2) above may also include extensions of the following additional type:

(6) Tail end alternate

(7) Tail end dry type

(8) Deluge

1 Wet pipe system

In this type of system, all the pipes that lead from the water supplies through the various controlling valves to the sprinkler heads throughout the building are kept permanently filled with water. Wet pipe systems are installed in premises where there is no danger, at any time, of the water in the pipes freezing. The principle controls of such a system are:

(i) a stop valve on each separate source of supply;

(ii) a non-return valve on each source of supply;

(iii) an installation main stop valve to cut off the flow of water to the system after a head has opened and the fire has been extinguished;

(iv) an alarm valve which lifts when water enters the sprinkler pipes allowing water to pass to the alarm gong; this valve also acts as a non-return valve to prevent the return flow of water from the sprinkler pipes to the supply connections;

(v) a test and drain valve, used for testing the water flow of the installation and to empty the system when necessary. The size of this valve is 40mm in LH installations and 50mm in OH and HH installations.

a. Types of wet pipe installations

In Fig. 3.1, a typical wet pipe installation is shown and it can be seen that there are two sources of supply, one from the towns mains (1) and the other from a secondary source supply (2). Both are fitted with stop-valves and non-return valves to ensure that water from either supply will not flow into the other. These supplies unite in the main supply pipe (3) which is fitted with a main stop valve (4).

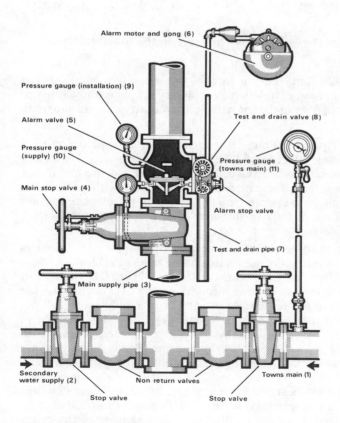

Fig. 3.1 A wet pipe system showing the main valve and gauges.

Above the main stop valve is an alarm valve (5) from which a pipe is led off to the alarm motor and gong. When the alarm valve functions some water passes through the annular groove in the alarm valve seating to the water turbine causing it to rotate and the clapper to strike the gong.

Adjacent to the alarm valve there is a test and drain pipe (7) and the discharge from the pipe is controlled by a test and drain valve (8).

There are three gauges:

(i)   gauge (9) showing the pressure in the installation above the mains stop and alarm valves;

(ii) gauge (10) showing the pressure of the supply below the main stop valves;

(iii) gauge (11) which shows pressure in the towns mains

A gauge indicating the pressure of the secondary supply is not considered necessary unless the secondary supply is a towns main. Secondary supplies in the form of pumps require pressure gauges to be fitted.

Another type of wet pipe system coming into use incorporates a 'butterfly' clack valve. Fig. 3.2 (1.) illustrates the general layout and the configuration of the valve. Fig. 3.2 (2.) shows the method of compensating for a fluctuation in mains pressure without allowing the turbine alarm to operate. Fig. 3.2 (3.) demonstrates the position of the clack valve fully open when a sprinkler operates. Plate 2 shows a valve-group in position.

Wet pipe systems are designed so that the number of sprinklers controlled by one set of valves (including tail end extensions) does not exceed 500 in the LH systems or 1000 in OH or HH systems; this latter figure is inclusive of any sprinkler on any LH systems. In a life safety installation the number of sprinklers is reduced to 200 per zone (see chapter 1 (6)). In calculating the total number of sprinklers in wet pipe systems, any in concealed places or in machines may be ignored. Where more heads than this are installed, two or more sets of installation valves should be used. Each set of valves must be numbered clearly and the appropriate alarm gong must bear the same number. In wet pipe installations, the heads may be installed in either the upright (above the range pipes) or pendant position (fitted to the underside of the range pipes).

How the BW valve works

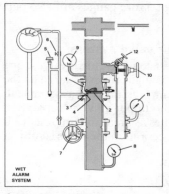

1 Town main and installation pressure in balance

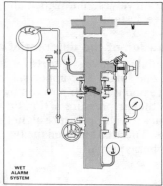

2 Slight increase in town main pressure (Alarm port sealed/clack in compensating position).

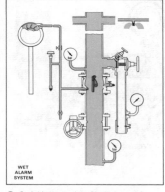

3 Sprinkler operating. Clack open and alarms operating

1 Butterfly valve body.
2 Clack
3 Alarm portway
4 Alarm portway seal
5 Pressure switch (Alarm)
6 Hydaulic alarm isolating valve
7 Installation stop valve
8 Water pressure gauge
9 Installation pressure gauge
10 Water proving test valve
11 Proving pipe flow gauge
12 Weekly test valve

Fig. 3.2 'Butterfly' wet pipe installation. (1) Illustrates general lay-out. (2) Compensating for a fluctuation in pressure. (3) Valve fully open when sprinkler head is open.

2   Dry pipe system

Dry pipe installation are installed where the temperature conditions are artificially maintained close to, or below freezing point e.g. cold stores, or where the temperature is maintained above 70°C. The pipes are, at all times, kept charged with air under sufficient pressure to hold back the water supply. Only upright or dry pendant sprinklers are fitted in this type of system.

Controlling valves of a dry pipe system are, usually a main stop valve and a differential air valve, which is the substitute for the alarm valve in a wet system. An hydraulic alarm motor and gong, test and drain valves, alarm cock and pressure gauges are also part of the valve system.

a. Operation of the differential air valve system

A differential air valve system (Fig. 3.3) consists of two valves, one large and one small. The upper valve is eight times as large as the lower valve and is held in position by air pressure and a water seal. In theory the air pressure acting on the upper valve is capable of holding back a water pressure eight times as great, but in practice it is little less. The area between the two sections of the valve is subject to atmospheric pressure.

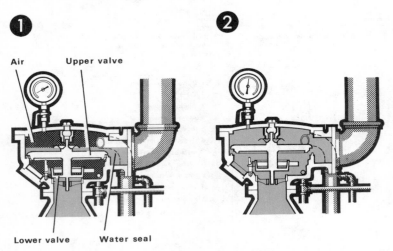

Fig. 3.3 The differential air valve of a dry pipe system. (1) In the closed position. (2) In the open position.

When a sprinkler head opens, the compressed air escapes reducing the pressure on the upper valve, allowing the lower valve to open and water to enter the system and emerge at the open sprinkler head. There is some delay before the water reaches the sprinkler head because of the time required to release sufficient air from the system to allow the valve to open and water to enter and travel up the pipe to the open sprinkler head. A device, known as an accelerator, is therefore normally fitted or a special type of valve is incorporated. The function of both is to speed up the entry of water into the system. It is undesirable to maintain a greater air pressure in the system than is necessary, and approximately one-third to one-half of the maximum water pressure is the normal figure. Provision is made for replacing any slight leakage that takes place.

b. Action of the accelerator

The action of the accelerator varies with each make of differential valve. One type fitted to a Mather and Platt alternate system is shown below.

The accelerator consists of two vessels normally filled with air at the same pressure as that of the installation. The lower vessel (Fig. 3.4(1)) is connected directly to the installation through the pipe (2), but the upper vessel (3) has no direct communication with the installation except through the pinhole (4). When a sprinkler head operates, pressure in the upper vessel and the inter-connecting air chamber (5) falls less rapidly than the lower vessel. Soon, therefore, the pressure exerted on each side of the diaphragm (6) becomes unequal and the diaphragm moves away from the air chamber. In doing so, it pushes the plunger (7) which in turn knocks over the bobweight (8) that opens the valve (9), thus allowing air to pass through the lower vessel, through the pipe (2) to the pipe (10), as shown by the arrows in Fig. 3.4 (right).

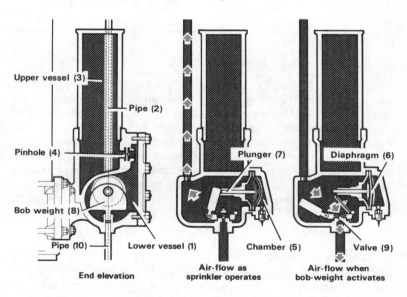

Fig. 3.4 Diagram showing the principles underlaying the operation of an accelerator.

The pipe (10) leads into the atmospheric chamber between the upper and lower valves in the differential air valve and the pressure of the air entering the chamber quickly neutralises the pressure holding the upper valve down, thus speeding up the opening process.

When an accelerator is fitted, the time taken for the water to reach the fire is reduced from about 2.5 minutes to about 20 seconds. It will still take a little time for the water to reach the actuated sprinkler head.

c. Maximum number of sprinklers

The maximum number of sprinklers controlled by one set of valves on a dry pipe system is shown in Table 5 below.

Table 5
Number of sprinklers permitted on dry pipe and alternate systems controlled by one set of valves

	light hazard systems	Ordinary and/or high hazard systems
With accelerator	250	500
Without accelerator	125	250

3   Alternate wet and dry system

This system is usually installed in premises that are without adequate artificial heating and where water in a wet system would be liable to freeze during cold weather. The system usually operates on a wet principle in the summer months and dry principle in the winter. When functioning on the wet system, the dry valve is either changed over or placed out of commission and the system functions as a wet system. Changing the system from one method of operation to the other can be effected quickly. A wet system is to be preferred since statistics show that when fires occur, a greater number of heads open when the system is on air, due to the delay in water reaching the first sprinkler head affected.

a. Sprinkler heads

In dry pipe and alternate systems the heads are always place above the distributing pipes, which are themselves given a slight slope so that water will not be trapped in pockets when the the system is drained. The only exception to this rule which is allowed is if approved dry pendant pattern sprinklers are installed or where standard sprinkler erected pendants have an approved anti-freeze device incorporated in them.

b. Valve assembly

A typical alternate system valve assembly with the valve clacks lifting vertically on a central spindle is shown in Fig. 3.5. This pattern has the accelerator (1) separate from the main part of the assembly.

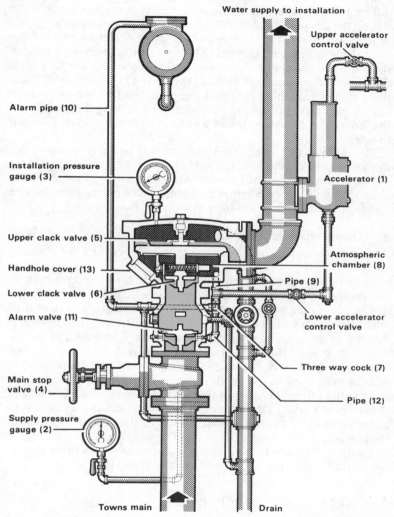

Fig. 3.5 Cross-section through the air valve and alarm valve of an alternate sprinkler system.

When set up as in Fig. 3.5, the pipes of the installation are filled with air. The pressure is shown on the supply pressure gauge (2) and the air pressure on the installation gauge (3). The main stop valve (4) is open and the water is held back by the differential air valve (5 and 6), as described on page 22.

25

c. Three-way cock

It should be noted that the three-way cock (Fig. 3.5(7)) is adjusted differently when the installation is on the wet pipe system than when it is on the dry pipe system. When on the dry pipe system, as shown in the illustration, the three-way cock must be set to allow water from the atmospheric chamber (8) to flow through the pipe (9) and then into the alarm pipe. On a wet system, however, the pipe (9) is disconnected and, as soon as the alarm valve (11) is actuated, water flows through the pipe (12) past the cock and into the alarm pipe (10). The correct setting can be obtained by making the grooves on the face of the cock correspond with the water passages it is desired to open.

The double clack of the air valve can only be reset by hand. For this purpose the hand hole cover (13) is provided. This cover must not be removed to reset the valve until the main stop valve (4) has been shut and the installation drained; otherwise the room where the valves are located will immediately be flooded.

d. Other types of alternate systems

Another type of alternate system is that incorporating the butterfly valve.

In this system the butterfly valve is held in the closed position by the pressure on a diaphragm and spindle assemble adjacent to it.

The alternate, or dry systems, are fitted with an accelerator, which works on a similar principal to that illustrated in Fig. 3.4. It is divided into two chambers and, under dry conditions, in the sprinkler system the air pressure is equalised between the two chambers their only connection being a restricted orifice. On operation of a sprinkler the air pressure in the installation and the top chamber drops faster than that in the lower chamber because of the restricted orifice. Because of the unequal pressure a diaphragm in the accelerator inverts, opening a valve, allowing air to equalise the pressure on both sides of the diaphragm holding the clack valve in position. The clack valve opens under pressure of the water, is latched open and the water flows to the sprinkler.

4 Tail-end systems (dry pipe or alternate)

These systems are essentially similar to those previously described, except that they are of comparatively small extent and form extensions to standard sprinkler installations. They are permitted:

(a) As extensions to a wet pipe system in comparatively small areas (i) where there is possible frost danger in an otherwise adequately heated building, and (ii) in high temperature areas or stoves. The tail-end would be on the alternate wet and dry principle in the case of (i) and on the dry pipe principle for (ii).

(b) As extensions to an alternate wet and dry system in high temperature areas or stoves, when tail-end systems would be on the dry pipe principle.

Sprinklers in tail-end systems must be installed in the upright position above the lines of pipes, an exception being if approved dry pendant pattern sprinklers are installed.

The number of sprinklers in a group of tail-end systems controlled by one set of wet pipe system or alternate wet and dry pipe system valves, must not exceed 250 in total, with not more than 100 sprinklers on any one tail-end system. Each tail-end system must be provided with a 50mm drain valve and drain pipe. A pressure gauge must be fitted at a point above the seating of the tail-end valve. A subsidary stop valve may be fitted below the tail-end valve, providing it is of the interlocking key type and in a conspicuous position. When the valve is temporarily closed the key must be readily visible.

5   Pre-action systems

A pre-action system is a combination of a standard sprinkler system and an independent, approved system of heat or smoke detectors installed in the same area as the sprinklers. Heat and smoke detectors will, generally, operate prior to sprinklers and open a 'pre-action valve' to allow water to flow into a 'dry' system before the first sprinkler operates.

The idea of the pre-action valve is to prevent accidental discharge of water from sprinkler pipework following mechanical damage.

The maximum number of sprinklers controlled by a pre-action valve, whether it is in a heated or unheated building, is 500 for LH and 1000 for OH and HH systems. As is usual, operation of the detector system will automatically operate an alarm.

a.   General theory of on-off systems

Often in fires in sprinklered buildings, particularly where flammable liquids are involved or where the initial rate of burning of materials is very high, a large number of sprinkler heads will open. Many of these may be at a considerable distance, horizontally, from the burning materials and, although wetting materials around the fire area, their operation reduces the amount of water being applied to the actual fire.

If, consequently, the water density over the fire area decreases below the design density, the heat release remains undiminished and more sprinklers will open. There is now a 'domino' effect i.e. water density, generally, further diminishes, more sprinklers open etc. and the fire becomes uncontrollable.

Where a system of on-off sprinklers are fitted there is a possibility that those which operate outside the fire area in its early stages may close again following an initial application of water. This could have a reverse 'domino' effect i.e. sprinklers close around the fire area, increasing the water density actually over the fire, heat reduces still more, more heads close. Eventually, when the fire is extinguished, all sprinklers close and prevent further water damage.

Main advantages:

(i) Increased efficiency of a system whereby the water is concentrated in the immediate fire area

(ii) Reduced total of water required to extinguish the fire

(iii) Unecessary water damage prevented after the fire has been extinguished

(iv) The automatic resetting of this type of system does not leave premises exposed to a system shut-down awaiting reinstatement by a sprinkler engineer.

(v) Reduced possibility of a premature shut-down of a system before the fire is extinguished.

b. Types of systems

(i) General

There are two types of system:

(a) where the water-flow is controlled at the system operating valve (sometimes known as the re-cycling system).

(b) where the flow is controlled at the individual sprinkler heads.

(ii)

(a) Recycling systems

An example of a recycling system is one developed by the Viking Corporation and is called 'Firecycle'. A schematic layout is shown in Fig. 3.6 and comprises of a standard system of sprinkler pipework with normal sprinkler heads, a system of heat detectors and a flow control valve operated by solenoid valves. The system pipework is filled with air at a pressure of 1 bar.

When a fire occurs, the heat detectors which are set to operate at 57°C, trip and break the circuit at the control panel. The solenoid valves are de-energised and the pressure in the upper chamber of the flow control valve is released allowing the valve to open and water to flow into the system and also operate the motor-alarm gong. Further increase in the temperature to 68°C will operate the sprinkler heads and direct water onto the fire. When ceiling temperature drops below 57°C, the heat detectors remake the circuit to the control panel and, after a delay of 5 minutes, the solenoid valves are energised, the pressure in the upper chamber of the flow control valve increases and the valve closes, shutting off water to the sprinkler heads.

If the fire is not completely controlled the head detectors will again respond and repeat the cycle. The system is designed so that any electrical failure resulting in the loss of power to the solenoid valves causes them to open again and the system becomes an ordinary wet system.

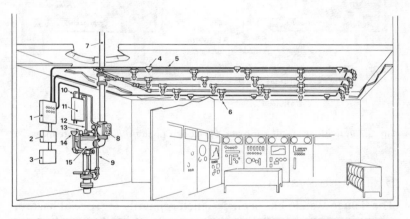

ITEM	DESCRIPTION	ITEM	DESCRIPTION	ITEM	DESCRIPTION	ITEM	DESCRIPTION
1	Control Panel	6	Sprinkler	11	Trim Box containing	14	Drain Cup
2	Battery Charger	7	Riser to Second Floor		Solenoids	15	Flow Control Valve
3	Batteries	8	Check Valve	12	Flow Control Valve		
4	Detector	9	Drain Pipe		Release & Set Line		
5	Detector Cable	10	Piping to Check Valve	13	Water Gauge 2		

Fig. 3.6 Schematic diagram of 'Firecycle' re-cycling sprinkler system.

c. Individual on-off sprinkler heads

At the time of writing (1989) there are no LPC approved on-off sprinkler systems but firefighters may come across them neverthe-less. The Grinnell 'Aquamatic' is approved in the USA and is illustrated in Fig. 3.7. It uses a bi-metal snap disc which expands when heated to a pre-determined temperature and withdraws a pilot valve slightly. This releases some water from beneath the piston assembly and allows it to drop. Water can then pass into the body of the sprinkler and strike the deflector. When the temperature falls the bi-metal snap disc returns to its normal position shutting off the sprinkler.

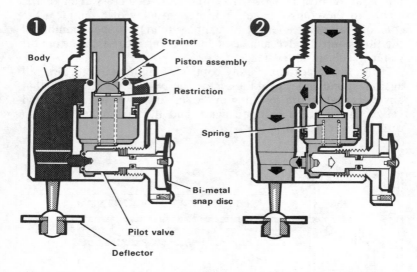

Fig. 3.7 Individual on-off sprinkler. (1) closed position. (2) open position.

6   Deluge systems

The deluge system has been designed primarily for special hazards where intensive fires with a very fast rate of fire propagation are expected, and it is desirable to apply water simultaneously over a complete zone in which a fire may originate. This is a system of open sprinklers controlled by a quick-opening valve, operated by approved heat detectors or sprinklers installed in the same area as the open sprinklers.

Quartzoid bulb detectors (Fig. 3.8) are mounted in an independent pipework system containing compressed air, so positioned that wherever a fire may start, one at least will operate and allow the compressed air in the pipework to escape. This causes a rapid fall in pressure on the diaphragm in the automatic deluge valve, to which both systems of pipework are connected. The movement of the diaphragm causes the deluge valve to open and water to discharge through the projectors.

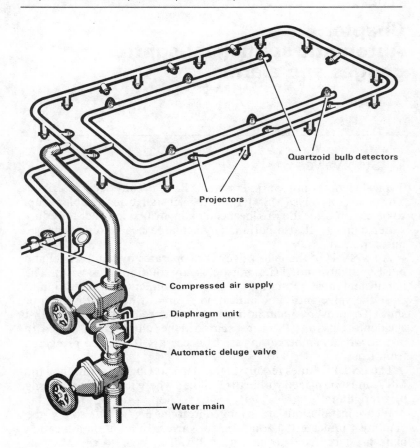

Fig. 3.8 Diagram of a typical deluge system.

Chapter 4
Automatic sprinklers: controls, gauges and alarms

1 Stop Valves

Typical layouts of the various systems have already been described. The main stop valve (MSV), fitted to all installations, enables water to be cut off after the fire has been extinguished in order to reduce water damage. It also permits any actuated heads to be removed and replaced.

An MSV is of the gate valve type, operates by hand-wheel and must be right-handed (i.e. must close by rotating clock-wise). The handwheel must be marked to show the direction of operation to close the valve and some indication given of whether it is open or shut. To prevent unauthorised interference and guard against accidental closure, MSVs are secured in the fully open position with a strap which can be cut in case of necessity. It must be protected from frost.

The BS/LPC Rules require that a plan showing the position of the MSVs must be placed within the building where it can be seen easily by firefighters.

Where installations are arranged in zones e.g. for life safety, the plan must indicate the zone control valves. In addition a location plate must be fixed to an external wall as near to the MSV as

Fig. 4.1 A type of sprinkler location plate.

possible. It must bear the legend shown in (Fig. 4.1) in letters not less than 35mm in height, preferably in white on a black background.

Where possible the MSV must be placed close to an entrance to the premises, preferably the main entrance, in such a location as to be always readily visible to authorised persons.

In addition to the MSV, each supply to the system is fitted with a stop valve (see Fig. 3.1). Subsidary stop valves may be used on certain sections of an installation to facilitate the testing of a dry-pipe valve, when a system is permanently on a dry system or to control sprinklers on a tail-end dry pipe system. The valves are of the interlocking key type and when the valves are closed the key is readily visible.

2 Non-return valves

The principle upon which a non-return valve works is shown in detail in Fig. 4.2. Water can pass through the valve, only in the direction of the arrows, by raising the clack valve. Any tendency to cause a flow of water in the reverse direction forces the clack valve on to its seating and so closes the valve.

Each water supply must be fitted with such a valve, unless there is only a single connection for the installation, when a non-return valve is unnecessary. A few water undertakings insist on the provision of a non-return valve on a single town main connection as an additional safeguard against the return of water from a sprinkler installation into the main. Non-return valves may be placed near the main stop valve, but are most frequently found close to the supply stop valve at the point of entry of the supply into the premises.

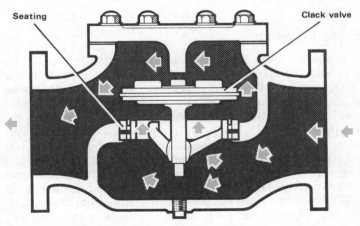

Fig. 4.2 Section through a non-return valve.

Non-return valves are fitted to prevent a reverse flow in the supply system due to the unequal pressures at which they operate. For example, if a town main, having a good pressure, and an elevated tank are used as water supplies to a sprinkler system, water from the main would, unless a non-return were fitted, pass up the supply connecting the tank to the installation and cause it to overflow.

3 Drain valves and test valves

A pipe is led from the side of the alarm valve, in wet installations, and from the air chamber of the differential air valve, in dry or alternate systems, into a drain. The pipe is fitted with a valve and the pipe and valve are used to drain the system when necessary and also carry out pressure and flow tests. The diameter of the pipe will depend upon the hazard rating of the occupancy.

With systems supplied by town main elevated reservoirs and gravity tanks, facilities must be provided to enable 'proving tests' to be carried out at the valves of each installation. This is to verify that the water supply satisfies the requirements of pressure and rates of flow specified for the particular hazard class (see Table 4). The proving tests must be carried out by the installing engineers at the time the system is installed and subsequently as required. The installation drain pipework (Fig. 4.3) is specifically designed to be used for the proving test.

4 Pipe drains

In some installations part of the sprinkler piping is below the control valves and drain cocks are fitted at the lower parts of the piping so that they may be completely drained as necessary.

5 Pressure gauges

Every sprinkler system must be fitted with a pressure gauge (Fig. 4.3(1)) above the alarm valve, and this shows the pressure in the installation (which will be water pressure when the system is on water, and air pressure when on air). Another gauge (2) must also be fitted below the alarm and main stop valve, and this indicates the water supply pressure. When a connection from a town main forms one of the duplicate water supplies, a gauge (not shown in Fig. 4.3) must also be fixed on the branch from the main on the town side of the back-pressure valve. This gauge shows the pressure in the town main. The reading of this latter gauge may be lower than that of the gauge (2) depending upon the pressure available from the secondary supply. A supply from a pump is also fitted with a pressure gauge on the down side of the non-return valve.

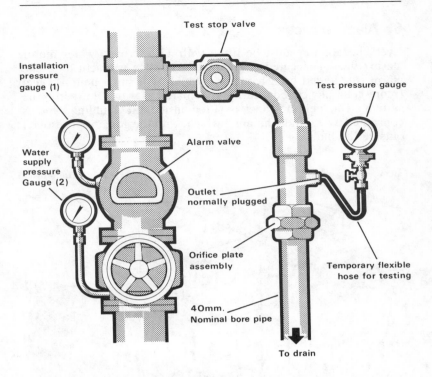

Fig. 4.3 Diagram showing the arrangement of installation proving equipment (for extra light hazard).

The gauges used are normally of the Bourdon tube type and conform to BS 1780. There must be means provided to enable each pressure gauge to be readily removed without interruption of installation water supplies.

The pressure indicated on the gauge (1) connected above the alarm valve is sometimes higher than that on gauge (2) below the main stop valve. This is due to the fact that, after the system has been charged with water, a rise in pressure in the town main causes the alarm valve to lift and admit pressure to the installation. When, however, the main's pressure falls again, the pressure in the installation is retained by the alarm valve which is, of course, a non-return valve. The difference in pressure sometimes results in a slight delay in the sounding of the alarm gong. When a sprinkler head opens, it is necessary for the pressure in the installation to fall below that in the main before the alarm valve opens and allows water to flow to the water turbine of the alarm.

6 Alarm devices

Every installation must be fitted with an approved water motor alarm (Fig. 4.4), located as near the alarm valve as practicable. The alarm is sounded by a hammer rotated by a small pelton wheel (more generally called a turbine) actuated as water flows into the system. The pelton wheel is fitted inside the building, and is connected by a spindle hammer which, with the gong, is positioned outside the building.

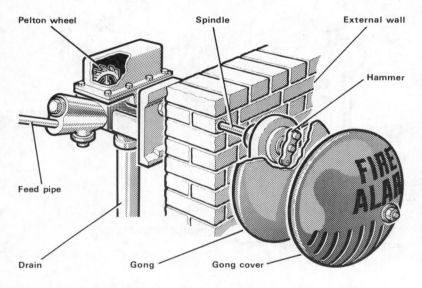

Fig. 4.4 An arrangement of a sprinkler gong and the turbine which actuates it.

The gong is usually placed above and close to the doorway that leads to the main stop valve. Where more installations are fitted to that same building, each has its own gong. Each gong must be numbered in bold figures to correspond with the number painted on the controlling valves of each installation. The flow of water to the turbine may also actuate an electric alarm at central point and so give immediate information as to the particular installation that has operated.

There are four causes which may produce a ringing of the alarm gong:

(i)   the opening of a sprinkler head;

(ii)   the opening of a drain or test valve;

(iii)   damage to any part of the installation which leads to an outflow of water;

(iv)   a rise in the pressure of the water being supplied to the installation, thus lifting the alarm valve and allowing water to pass to the turbine operating the gong.

As a precaution against false alarms caused by spasmodic increases of pressure in the town main, most alarm valves contain a small compensating device which permits small quantities of water to pass through the installation without lifting the clack. The pipe to the water turbine can be fitted with a device known as an 'alarm delay cylinder' which comprises an air bottle fitted with a drain orifice to which the alarm valve connection is led and from which the water turbine is supplied.

If the alarm clack lifts momentarily the air bottle is unlikely to fill with water, and thus a false alarm is prevented. When the alarm valve resets, the water drains from the delay cylinder through the drain valve. Another device is shown in Fig. 4.5. This device

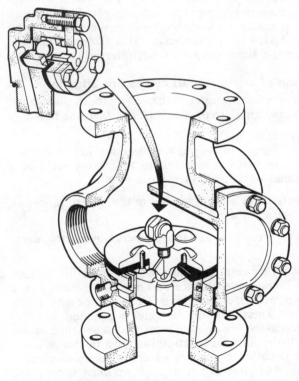

Fig. 4.5 Compensating device on a clack valve which allows a small quantity of water to pass without lifting the clack.

prevents false alarms without delaying, to any appreciable extent, the operation of the water turbine when the alarm clack valve is lifted where a sprinkler has actuated, or during a periodical alarm test. Alternatively, a small semi-rotary hand-pump can be fitted to the installation supply pipe and the pressure in the installation can be raised a little above the supply pressure by hand pumping.

In a wet pipe system, the gong may continue to sound after testing owing to a piece of grit becoming lodged under the seat of the alarm valve. Opening the drain valve fully will probably cause the obstruction to be washed away; if not, it may be necessary to close the main stop valve, drain the installation, remove the valve cover and thoroughly clean the alarm valve. The gong may continue to sound if the alarm valve seat has become scored or pitted so as to allow water to flow continuously.

a. Electrically-operated alarms

Approved water flow alarm switches may be incorporated in the system pipework above the alarm or dry pipe valve to indicate on a central control panel the particular section of the system which is operating. Electric alarm pressure switches, operated at either an increase or fall in pressure, are permitted on a system to operate an auxiliary warning device, but are not accepted as a substitute for the standard water motor alarm device already referred to.

b. Transmission of alarm signals to the fire brigade

Arrangements may be incorporated in the system for the automatic transmission of alarm signals to the fire brigade. Alarm signals may be initiated:

(i) by a flow of water in the sprinkler system using an electric alarm pressure switch connected to the alarm valve in a similar manner to the sprinkler alarm motor;

(ii) by using water flow alarm switches in the system pipework above the alarm valve;

(iii) by a fall in pressure in the system pipework above the alarm valve.

Pressure switches for transmitting alarm signals to the fire brigade must be suitable for sprinkler service and must be mounted on a vertical branch pipe at least 300mm long. They must be sufficiently sensitive to operate when only one sprinkler is actuated.

If the connection to the fire brigade is severed at any time as, for example, during hydraulic testing, attention must be drawn automatically to this situation by means of conspicuous duplicated warning lights linked to a buzzer warning. Means must be provided to prevent false alarms occuring with water supplies which are subject to fluctuation in pressure.

The system wiring and power supply must conform to the requirements laid down in BS 5839 Pt 4 1988. A test of:

(i)   the fire brigade or RMC connections;

(ii)   the circuit between the alarm switch and the control unit; and

(iii)   the batteries,

must be made every weekday (except holidays). The first two tests need only be made once a week provided the circuits used are continuously monitored. A notice must be fixed close to the sprinkler test valves of each installation to indicate a direct alarm connection to the fire brigade.

On sprinkler systems where arrangements are incorporated for the automatic transmission of alarm signals to the fire brigade, the arrangements will be regarded as approved by the BS/LPC if they comply with certain conditions, as follows:

(i)   there must be either a connection directly or through a RMC, approved by the BS/LPC and from there to a local authority fire station manned by whole-time personnel, or part-time retained personnel alerted by call-out systems; or

(ii)   a direct connection to a permanently manned watchroom of a private fire brigade.

The direct line from the premises whether to the fire brigade control, approved RMC or private fire brigade must terminate in a watchroom or control room permanently manned day and night.

Chapter 5
Automatic sprinklers: sprinkler heads

There are many different designs of sprinkler head but they may be generally divided into two categories:

(i)   those in which the operating medium is a fusible solder;

(ii)   those in which a bulb is ruptured by the expansion of a contained fluid (see Plate 3).

For normal occupancy situations, in temperate countries, the recommended operating temperature for sprinkler heads is 68°C.

1   Fusible solder type

A head of this type is shown in Fig. 5.1. The deflector (1) designed to spread the water issuing from the orifice, is supported by the two arms of the yoke (2) which screws into the body of the sprinkler which is itself, screwed into the pipe. Held in place by the yoke is a flexible metal diaphragm (3) with a hole in the centre over which fits a valve (4) of glass or gunmetal. Over the valve is fitted a metal cap

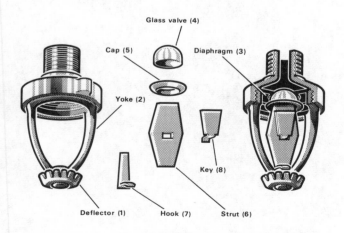

Fig. 5.1 One type of fusible solder type sprinkler head.

(5) which contains a notch into which the end of the strut (6) is inserted. The strut is supported by two other metal plates: the hook (7), the curved end of which engages the deflector end of the yoke, and the key (8). These three parts are held rigidly together by a special fusible solder and keep the valve cap in position against the pressure in the piping which acts upon the other side of the diaphragm. When the temperature surrounding the head rises to a level at which the solder is heated to its fusing point, the strut, hook and key fly apart owing to the strain under which they are held. The valve cap is released and allows the water an uninterrupted passage to the deflector.

In another type (Fig. 5.2) the metal parts holding the valve cap in place are constructed on the cantilever principle. Here two cantilever members pivoted on one another are connected by a

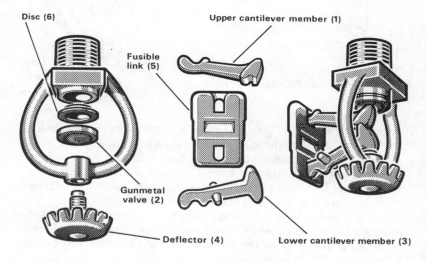

Fig. 5.2 Second type of fusible solder sprinkler head which operates on a cantilever principle.

fusible link placed outside the arms of the yoke. The upper member (Fig. 5.2(1)) is socketed in the gunmetal valve (2), and the lower member (3) in a slot of the adjustable screw assembly in the deflector boss (4), which enables tension to be given to the cantilever members. When the fusible link (5) melts, the members are thrown clear of the head, additional thrust being given by the pressure of the water on air behind the disc (6) which is held in place over the orifice by the valve (2).

41

A third type of soldered sprinkler head is illustrated in Fig. 5.3. This shows how a soft metal gasket and valve, which form the watertight joint, are supported by a soft metal strut, which is

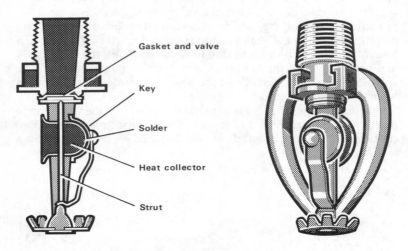

Gasket and valve

Key

Solder

Heat collector

Strut

Fig. 5.3 Third type of fusible solder sprinkler head.

retained in position so long as the hemispherical key remains held to the heat collector by the special solder used for this purpose. When a fire occurs, the temperature of the heat collector rises until the solder melts to release the key. The hook and key then spring outwards and, together with the strut, valve and gasket, are thrown clear to allow the discharge of water on to the deflector.

Fusible metal type heads are supplied to operate at various temperatures (see Table 6). The fusing temperature of a soldered sprinkler is stamped on the metal strut and the yoke arm can be coloured as shown in the Table.

N.B. SPRINKLER HEADS MAY BECOME UNCERTAIN IN THEIR OPERATION IF THE NORMAL AMBIENT TEMPERATURE APPROACHES TOO CLOSELY TO OPERATING TEMPERATURE. THE TEMPERATURE RATING CHOSEN SHOULD THEREFORE BE AS CLOSE AS POSSIBLE TO, BUT NOT LESS THAN, 30°C ABOVE THE HIGHEST ANTICIPATED AMBIENT TEMPERATURE.

Table 6
Ratings and colours of fusible metal sprinkler heads

Rating of Sprinkler	Colour of yoke arm
68 to 74°C	Uncoloured
93 to 100°C	White
141°C	Blue
182°C	Yellow
227°C	Red

2 Bulb type

In the bulb type head (Fig. 5.4), a small barrel or cylinder made of special glass is used to hold the water valve in place. This bulb is hermetically sealed and contains a quantity of liquid and a small bubble. As the temperature rises, the liquid expands and the size of the bubble decreases until it disappears. A further rise shatters the bulb, breaking it into small pieces so that it cannot obstruct the water flow, and so opens the head. In spite of this ease of fracture, the strength of the bulb is such that it can withstand any pressure applied to the pipe. In the pressure destruction test, it is the metal parts of the head that fail first.

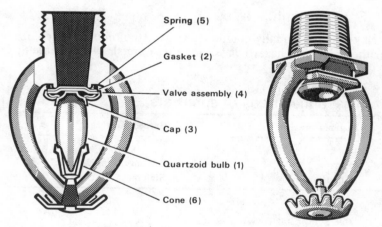

Spring (5)

Gasket (2)

Valve assembly (4)

Cap (3)

Quartzoid bulb (1)

Cone (6)

Fig. 5.4 Bulb type sprinkler head.

The gasket (2) is held in position by the bulb (1) which rests at one end upon a hollow in the valve cap (3) which in its turn is held in place by a valve assembly (4) and a spring (5) in order that is will throw the parts clear. At the other end the bulb is held in a conical metal cup (6).

43

By adjusting the composition of the liquid and to some extent the size of the bubble, the bulb type head can be set to operate at any desired temperature. Those most commonly employed are shown in Table 7.

Table 7
Standard bulb filling colours for various rating of bulb-type sprinkler heads

Sprinkler rating	Colour of bulbs
57°C	Orange
68°C	Red
79°C	Yellow
93°C	Green
141°C	Blue
182°C	Mauve
204 to 260°C	Black

Firefighters may also find in certain occupancies, a sprinkler fitted with a very thin bulb. This is described as a 'fast-response' type (see section 4) but operates in the same way as the conventional quartzoid bulb

3   Sprinkler orifice sizes

Sprinklers are normally manufacturered with nominal orifice sizes for the respective hazard class, and these are shown in Table 8.

Table 8
Nominal orifice sizes of sprinklers

Nominal size	Hazard class
10 mm	Light only
15 mm	Ordinary and high only
20 mm	High only

4   Types of sprinkler head

a.   General
Sprinklers must be of a type approved by the BS/LPC Rules. After despatch from the production factory they must not be altered in any respect or have any ornamentation or coating applied. An approved coating for anti-corrosion purposes is allowed provided it is not applied to any glass bulb.

b. Approved types

The BS/LPC specify the following types of sprinkler heads:

(i)   conventional pattern

(ii)   spray pattern

(iii)   ceiling or flush pattern

(iv)   recessed pattern

(v)   concealed pattern

(vi)   sidewall pattern

c. Conventional pattern

This type produces a spherical type of discharge with a proportion of the water thrown upwards to the ceiling (see Plate 4). They may be installed upright (Fig. 5.5(i)) or pendant (Fig. 5.5(2)).

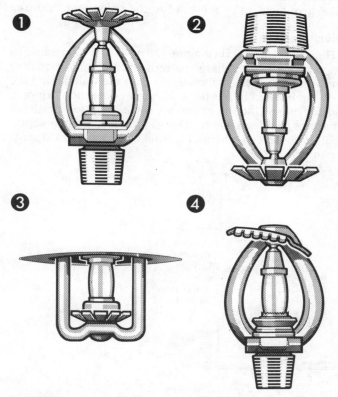

Fig. 5.5 Types of sprinkler. (1) Dry upright type. (2) Dry pendant pattern. (3) Ceiling flush pattern. (4) Sidewall pattern.

d. Spray pattern

A hemispherical discharge below the plane of the deflector is produced by this type with little or no discharge upwards to the ceiling. An upright version is also available.

e. Ceiling or flush pattern

This type (Fig. 5.5(3)) is for use with concealed pipework. The heads are installed pendant with the plate, or base, flush to the ceiling but with the heat-sensitive element below the ceiling line. They are also allowed to be installed in light or ordinary light hazard areas.

f. Recessed and concealed pattern

These types are similar to those described above in e. The concealed pattern however is recessed almost level with the ceiling line and is covered by a plate (Fig. 5.6). In a fire situation the solder holding the plate in position melts allowing the plate to fall away and expose the heat-sensitive element of the head to the rising temperature.

g. Sidewall pattern

This type (Fig.5.5(4)) is installed along the walls of a room close to the ceiling. It produces a discharge pattern resembling one quarter of a sphere with a proportion discharging onto the wall behind the sprinkler. It can be used in positions where condensation dripping from sprinkler pipework might be a problem or for aesthetic reasons or access problems where ceiling sprinklers are unacceptable. Sidewall sprinklers should not be installed in high hazard areas above suspended ceilings.

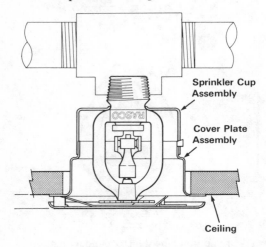

Sprinkler Cup
Assembly

Cover Plate
Assembly

Ceiling

Fig. 5.6 Recessed and concealed pattern of sprinkler head.

h. Fast-response sprinkler heads (FRS)

Normal sprinkler heads have fixed operating temperatures and their design is such that they are usually slower to react than electrical detectors. In recent years certain hazards or types of premises have required not only fast detection but fast control and thought has turned to changing the design of sprinkler heads to enable this to be done. Three diverse examples of areas where these type of heads are desirable are high-bay warehouses, residential care premises and (at present only in the USA) private homes. In these cases the amount of heat generated needs to be sensed, retained and conveyed to the bulb or soldered strut more quickly either to avoid the unusual rate of spread (high-bay warehouse) or to save lives (residential premises).

(i)   Design

Fusible strut type (FRS)

The first fusible strut types were fitted with additional heat collecting fins and later there were supplemented by having chrome-on-copper construction to transmit the heat to a greatly reduced amount of solder (Fig. 5.7) and (Plate 5).

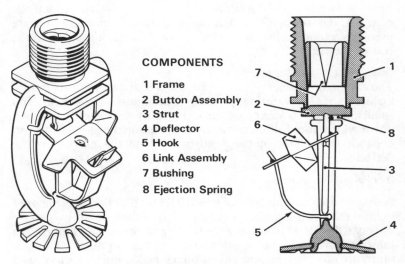

COMPONENTS

1 Frame
2 Button Assembly
3 Strut
4 Deflector
5 Hook
6 Link Assembly
7 Bushing
8 Ejection Spring

Fig. 5.7 Fast-response fusible-strut type sprinkler head.

Various refinements to these early types are:

(a) copper fins to circulate the hot gases around the link;

(b) a very thin link construction (reducing thermal mass)

47

(c) the minimum amount of solder;

(d) a small amount of material which not only holds the link in place but insulates if from the strut thus stopping heat loss to the body of the head.

Bulb type (FRS)

In the bulb type similar refinements have been tried. In one the bulb is very thin and, as far as is possible, insulated from the body. In another the bulb is very thin but set at an angle in the head to place it further out into the hot gas flow whilst keeping it as far away from the body of the head as possible.

(ii) Discharge patterns

The configuration of the premises and where the heads are placed often dictates the type of FRS used. In high-bay storage for instance they will vary according to whether they are in-rack, over-rack, side-rack, zone controlled etc.

In residential care premises and private houses the discharge pattern could be as shown in Fig. 5.8. Water needs to be projected more horizontally to ensure it is above the fire and can take in such items as curtains and furniture which is often placed around the edge of the room. Another consideration, especially in care premises, could be the usual position of the bed in relation to the rest of the room.

(iii) Water droplet size

The factor of discharge has to be looked at carefully to ensure maximum visibility during the control/extinguishment period. Too small a droplet size can cause the water spray to drag ceiling smoke down which could hinder evacuation. The discharge density will depend on the size of the head orifice and the design for the deflector.

(iv) Further information

A disadvantage in this type of head (FRS) is that the material used to hold the struts together, over a period of time, tends to 'creep'. This has the effect of sometimes leading to premature failure of a joint or conversely, raising the operating temperature. Manufacturers are now tending towards bulb-type heads and there may need to be a much-reduced replacement period for these heads. As little as 4 years has been advocated.

At the time of writing only one FRS head has received BS/LPC approval but there are several more which are being tested and should be approved. Despite this there are quite a number of premises in the UK which are fitted with FRS heads of, as yet, a non-approved type.

Conventional Sprinkler Discharge

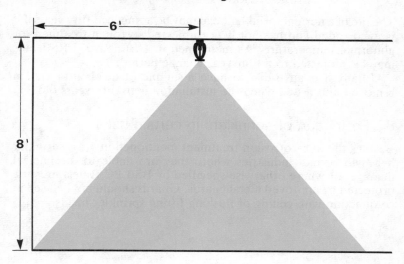

Residential Sprinkler Discharge

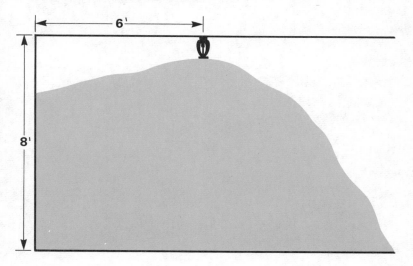

Fig. 5.8 Discharge patterns for conventional and residential sprinkler systems.

49

5   Life of sprinkler heads

The life of a normal sprinkler head may be as much as fifty years if it is uncorroded and has not been subjected to rough treatment or abnormal temperature. As mentioned in 4(h) above, FRS heads may be subjected to a four year change period.

Usually it is advisable to have a sample of heads in a system removed and tested when the installation is twenty years old.

6   Protection of sprinklers in certain risks

Besides the anti-corrosion treatment mentioned in 4(a), sprinkler heads in certain industries where they are liable to mechanical damage, or where otherwise specified by BS/LPC Rules, must be protected by approved metal guards. Guards should not be used in conjunction with ceiling of flushing fitting sprinkler heads.

Chapter 6
Automatic sprinklers: general

1 Siting of sprinkler heads

The following definitions are used to differentiate between the various pipework used on a sprinkler installation (Fig. 6.1).

(i)   Main distribution pipes: main pipes feeding the distribution pipework.

(ii) Distribution pipes: pipes directly feeding range pipes.

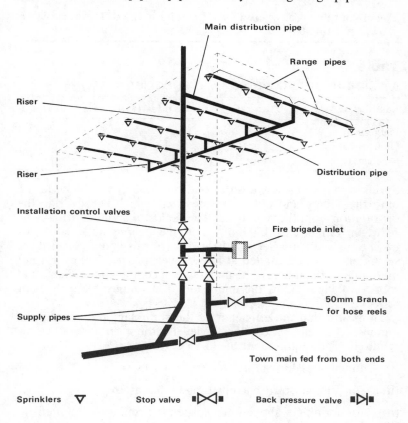

Fig. 6.1 Diagrammatic layout of the pipework of a sprinkler installation.

(iii)   Range pipes: pipes on which the sprinklers are attached either directly or on short arm pipes which do not exceed 300mm in length.

The number and layout of sprinklers allowed on range pipes depends on the layout and size of pipe used, but does not exceed nine on any one pipe. The number of sprinklers fed by a distribution pipe is also determined by the size of the pipe, with a maximum of 48 heads fed by one distribution pipe. Pipe sizes are determined hydraulically, partly by pre-calculated pipe size tables and partly by hydraulic calculation. The area covered by a sprinkler and the distance between sprinklers on range pipes and adjacent rows of sprinklers are determined by the hazard class of the installation.

2   Area covered by sprinklers

The maximum area covered by a sprinkler in the different classes is shown in Table 9.

Table 9

Maximum area covered by a sprinkler

Hazard class	General	Special risk areas or storage racks
Light hazard	$21m^2$	$9m^2$
Ordinary hazard	$12m^2$	$9m^2$
High hazard	$9m^2$	$9m^2$

Sprinkler design usually ensures that some water will be deflected onto the ceiling and out in a wide circle which will overlap the distribution from the next head. The deflector should normally be between 15mm and 150mm below the ceiling and roofs (for exceptions see Ch.5 Section 4(f)). Where this is not practicable, sprinklers may be installed at lower levels providing they are not more than 300mm below the underside of combustible ceilings and roofs or 450mm below the underside of incombustible ceilings or roofs.

To ensure that the efficiency of the sprinkler protection is not diminished a clear space below the level of the sprinkler deflector is required. The requirement of BS/LPC Rules is:

(i)   for high piled combustible stock – 1 metre

(ii)   for potable spirit barrel storage – 0.3 metre

(iii)   for sprinklers above open suspended ceilings – 0.8 metre

(iv)   for other than (i), (ii) or (iii) – 0.5 metre

Roof trusses must at all times, be accessible to water discharged from the sprinklers.

All parts of a building must be covered by sprinklers, otherwise fire can develop undetected for a period and become too large for the system to deal with effectively. Any roof space or floor space exceeding 800mm in depth must be sprinkler protected. Where holes are cut in floors to take machinery drives, conveyors, chutes and other vertical openings such as hoists, lifts, elevators, it is important that a sprinkler is sited above the opening on the upper floor in order that vertical spread of fire does not take place without early detection.

3 Multiple controls

Heat sensitive sealed valve control outlets (Fig. 6.2) are used when it is desired to operate small groups of sprayers simultaneously – hence the term multiple control.

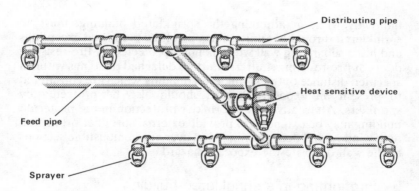

Fig. 6.2 Diagram of a multiple control system.

The heat sensitive device will be a glass bulb or a soldered link or lever. When this shatters or fuses, water is delivered to open sprayers which cover the protected area. An example of a control is shown in Fig. 6.3(1) and an open sprayer in Fig. 6.3(2). Where simultaneous operation on a larger scale is required a deluge system (similar to that shown in Fig. 8.5) will be fitted.

4 Extent of sprinkler system

Where a sprinkler system is installed, it must cover the whole building, except where the omission of sprinklers is specifically allowed under the rules. Every building communicating directly or

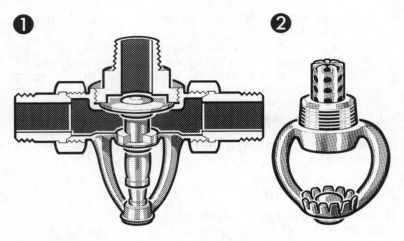

Fig. 6.3 (1) An automatic control. (2) An open sprayer.

indirectly with, or adjoining the sprinklered building, must be sprinklered throughout unless it is one of the permitted exceptions and has a separating wall with openings protected by fire-resisting doors or fire-resisting shutters. Certain detached buildings within a specified distance of the sprinklered building which are considered to present an exposure hazard should also be protected by sprinklers. Alternatively the sprinkler protection in the protected building may be extended to provide external sprinkler protection over window and door openings and over any combustible sections of the wall opposite the exposure hazard.

5   Firefighting in a sprinklered building

The following are the principal points a firefighter should bear in mind when fighting a fire in a sprinklered building:

(i)   On arrival at the fire, a member of the crew should immediately be sent to the main stop valve so that:

(a) the valve can be opened if found closed, and

(b) the valve is not closed except on the express instructions of the officer-in-charge.

Many so-called sprinkler failures have been due to premature closing of the main stop valve. A head opens and apparently extinguishes the fire, the water supply is cut off in order to prevent further water damage and the fire which has continued to smoulder in a hidden place later bursts out again. The premises being deprived of sprinkler protection, the fire grows to large proportions, possibly opening a number of heads. Should the valve then be re-opened the simultaneous discharge of water from these heads causes a drop in pressure and a less effective flow from each head. A sprinkler system is designed to check an incipient fire and not to cope with one that has got away.

(ii) On arrival at an installation where principal supplies of water can be augmented through a fire brigade inlet, a pump should be connected to the inlet ready to increase the pressure should a large number of heads have operated.

(iii) It should be remembered that there are many cases where sprinkers will satisfactorily hold the fire which can then be finally extinguished by firefighters using hose reels. The sprinklers should not normally be turned off in order that the fire may be fought with jets or spray branches.

(iv) If additional water is needed, it should not be taken from the main supplying the sprinklers unless it is of large size. This main will usually be a branch from a larger town main and pumps should be set into hydrants on the latter, or on a different main. The layout of mains supplying sprinkler installations in their areas should be known by local fire brigade officers.

(v) Although a sprinkler may appear to have extinguished the fire, careful examination of the area involved must be made in order to verify that no trace of fire remains.

(vi) When a fire is out and for any reason, it is impossible to turn off the main stop valve immediately and cut off the flow of water to the sprinkler head, water damage can be prevented by securing the female coupling of a length of hose over the head and leading the hose out of the window.

6 Re-setting of sprinkler systems

It is usual for brigades to issue specific orders that, following a fire in a sprinklered building, the occupiers are left with the responsibility for re-setting the system. This avoids any problems regarding insurance or adverse comment against the fire brigade should another fire occur and the system fail to operate.

Chapter 7
Protection of special risks

1 High-bay warehouse storage

a. General

The high-bay (or high racked) warehouse presents a particularly difficult type of fire risk, not only because of its size and height but also in the variety of goods stored in close proximity under one roof. The problem of providing efficient sprinkler protection for this type of building has been the subject of a great deal of research during recent years.

It has been found that ordinary in-rack sprinkler systems using conventional fusible solder or glass-bulb sprinklers give a generally unsatisfactory performance. Flames tend to pass a sprinkler location before its actual operation and ignite goods at a higher level, mainly due to the flue effect of the racking layout.

b. Design recommendations

An in-rack system incorporating a 'fast response' head (See Chapter 5) has proved more effective, especially when allied to recommendations on construction of the racking and positioning of heads.

These recommendations include:-

(i)   Range pipes located at alternate levels i.e. 2, 4, 6 etc, the top level being covered by a pipe above it.

(ii)   Fast response sprinklers located above the junction of transverse and longitudinal flues, pendant-mounted and incorporating a specially designed water-deflecting shield.

(iii)   A non-combustible covering (rack capping) located above the top level of goods with a range pipe and sprinklers located immediately below it.

(iv)   Partial capping of the side of the rack and the space between the end pallet position and the end of the rack.

(v)   In very high storage e.g. over 15m, intermediate rack capping to be considered with pipes and sprinklers underneath it.

(vi)   Certain minimum aisle widths to be maintained.

(vii)   The division of the protected area into a number of zones such that within each individual zone, all sprinklers operate together.

(viii) The hydraulic design of the system should be adequate for the height and area of each protected zone in the worst incident.

c. Categorisation of risks

High-piled storage (HPS), as found in these warehouses, comes under the high hazard (HH) category (See Chapter 1 Section 4c). For each of the sub-categories I-IV the BS/LPC have specified minimum densities of water application based on a formula. They consider, however, that there is a difference between HPS free-standing storage and HPS palletised-rack storage. The reason is that in a fire, free standing goods tend to break apart, allowing water to penetrate the stack. This does not readily happen in palletised rack storage and BS/LPC consider that this warrants an increased water density to protect it against fire. This has been done by requiring that commodities stored in this way (palletised) have their category increased by one-half except in the case of Group IV. Group IV requirements for water discharge density are already very large.

Table 10

Design density of discharge and assumed area of operation for high piled storage risks comprising palletised rack storage when roof or ceiling protection only is provided

DESIGN DENSITY OF DISCHARGE REQUIRED (MINIMUM) (mm/min)	ASSUMED MAXIMUM AREA OF OPERATION (m2)	STACK HEIGHT NOT EXCEEDING (METRES)			
		CATEGORY I	CATEGORY II	CATEGORY III	CATEGORY IV
7.5	260	4.7	3.4	2.2	1.6
10.0	260	5.7	4.2	2.6	2.0
12.5	260	6.8	5.0	3.2	2.3
15.0	260	–	5.6	3.7	2.7
17.5	260	–	6.0	4.1	3.0
–	–	–	–	–	–
20.0	300	–	–	4.4	3.3
25.0	300	–	–	5.3	3.8
30.0	300	–	–	6.0	4.4

Examples of goods in HPS categories are as follows (the categories are listed in order of increasing hazard);-

Category I   Wool carpets, textiles, electrical appliances

II   Baled waste paper, chipboard, plastics (non-foamed), wooden furniture.

III	Wax-coated paper, foamed plastics (except celluloid) rubber goods.
IV	Off-cuts of foam plastic, sheet foamed plastic, celluloid, foamed rubber.

Table 10 is an example of how BS/LPC rules are applied in discharge densities.

Table 11 and Fig. 7.1 illustrate typical requirements for sprinkler density in the four categories.

Table 11

Location of rack intermediate sprinklers according to category of goods

GOODS, EXTRA HIGH HAZARD CATEGORY	TIER PROTECTION		TRANSVERSE FLUE PROTECTION		SPRINKLER, SPACING PATTERN		MINIMUM CLEARANCE BETWEEN SPRINKLER DEFLECTOR AND TOP OF STORAGE IMMEDIATELY BELOW
	PROTECTION AT LEAST AT:	MAXIMUM VERTICAL DISTANCE BETWEEN LEVELS OF PROTECTION	POSITION OF SPRINKLERS ON LINES AT LEAST AT:	MAXIMUM HORIZONTAL DISTANCE BETWEEN SPRINKLERS ON LINES	SPRINKLERS AT ADJACENT PROTECTED TIER LEVELS		
					STAGGERED	RECTANGULAR MATRIX	
		M		M			MM
I	EVERY OTHER LEVEL	3.5	EVERY OTHER FLUE	2.8	√	-	150
II	EVERY OTHER LEVEL	3.5	EVERY OTHER FLUE	2.8	√	-	150
III*	EVERY OTHER LEVEL	3.5	EVERY FLUE	1.4	-	√	150
IV#	EVERY LEVEL	2.3	EVERY OTHER FLUE	2.8	√	-	150

* PLUS ANY MIX OF GOODS INCLUDING CATEGORY III AND LOWER CATEGORY GOODS

PLUS ANY MIX OF GOODS INCLUDING CATEGORY IV AND LOWER CATEGORY GOODS

2   Aircraft maintenance and assembly areas

a.   Ground level sprinklers

Protection of aircraft maintenance and assembly areas presents special problems, especially when dealing with fires under the large wing areas of modern commercial aircraft (see Manual, Book 4, Chapter 4).

The Filton aircraft maintenance area is a hangar 320 metres wide, 128 metres deep at the centre bay and 82 metres deep at each of the east and west bays. It is also 30 metres high.

To overcome the problem mentioned above, the hangar is fitted with sprinkler nozzles in the floor which raise and operate automatically in a fire situation. The area is divided into zones and each zone contains an average of 110 sprinklers. These are supplemented by wall-mounted, over-wing oscillating jets and the whole system is actuated by automatic radiation fire detectors.

The extinguishing agent is AFFF. The sprinklers each produce a vertical jet at least 5 metres high plus 3 peripheral jets giving a ground spray about 8 metres in diameter.

b. Portable units

During the assembly of large aircraft there are often portable fire detection and extinguishing units placed within the aircraft and linked to an outside control unit. Ionisation and heat detectors (linear and point) are used and the unit includes a BCF container which will be activated by the detectors.

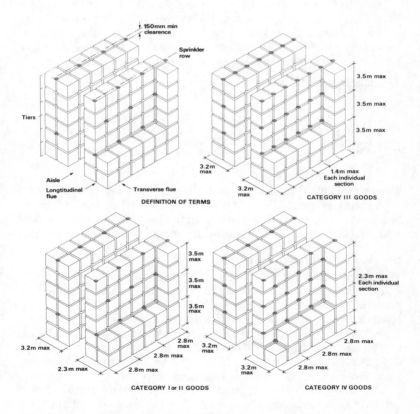

Fig. 7.1 Typical requirements for sprinkler density in the four categories of HPS storage.

Chapter 8
Other installations using water

1 Drenchers

While a sprinkler system protects a building from internal fire, drenchers are placed on roofs and over windows and external openings to protect the building from damage by exposure to a fire in adjacent premises. The layout of a typical drencher systems is shown in Fig. 8.1

A drencher system is comprised of water-heads somewhat similar to those of sprinklers; these may be sealed or unsealed (open-drenchers), but in the latter case the water is turned on manually. In a few instances drenchers may be controlled by quick-opening valves operated by loss of air pressure in a detector line system in a similar manner to high velocity water spray systems (see Section 2).

Drenchers are of three main types:

(a) Roof drenchers

(b) Wall drenchers

(c) Window drenchers

a. Roof drenchers

Roof drenchers (Fig. 8.2(1)) have a deflector rather similar to that of a sprinkler head. From the roof ridge they throw a curtain of water upwards which then runs down the roof. All parts of the roof and any skylights, windows or other openings must be protected.

b. Wall or curtain drenchers

Wall or curtain drenchers (Fig. 8.2(2)) throw water to one side only of the outlet in the form of a flat curtain over those openings or portions of a building most likely to admit fire. In order to cover all combustible portions of a wall, it is the usual practice to put a line of drenchers just below the eaves if these contain flammable material, and to fit every window or opening on the top two storeys with a drencher. Those below this level, except the ground floor and basement, are fitted on every alternate storey.

The drenchers must be fitted so that the streams form a water curtain which must come in contact with the window 600mm from the top. A special use for this type of drencher is on the stage side of a theatre proscenium arch to protect the safety curtain.

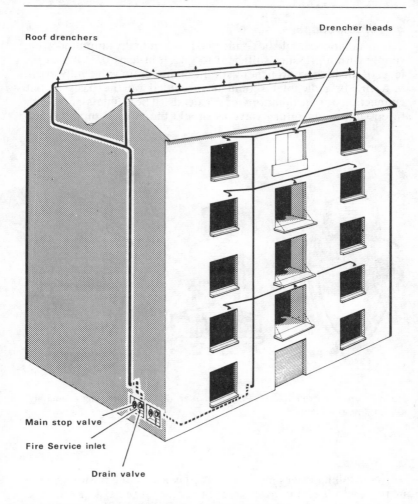

Roof drenchers

Drencher heads

Main stop valve

Fire Service inlet

Drain valve

Fig. 8.1 Diagram showing a typical drencher system.

c. Window drenchers

As their name implies, window drenchers (Fig.8.2(3)) are used to protect window openings. They are placed horizontally level with the top of the window, with the deflector 100mm from the surface of the wall providing a curtain of water to protect the glass. From the tail of the deflector, a jet is thrown inwards on to the glass near the top of the window, while two streams are directed at an angle of 45 degrees to the lower corners.

d. Water supplies

The installation should be connected to a nominally unlimited water supply with a pressure sufficient to give it at least 0.34 bar at the level of the highest drencher with the 50mm drain valve fully open.

A fire brigade inlet should be provided on the basis of one connection for installations of 55 heads. These inlets should be fitted with a non-return valve as should the normal supply type.

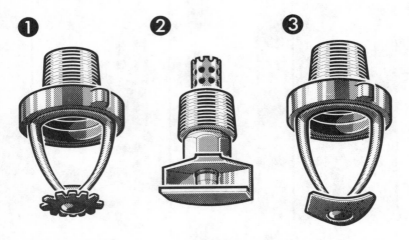

Fig. 8.2 Types of drencher. (1) Roof drencher. (2) Wall or curtain drencher. (3) Window drencher.

e. Valves

The controlling valves must be located in accessible positions on or near ground level but away from the adjacent fire risk. Protection from frost for the supply pipe and valves is essential. A padlocked or riveted strap must be used to secure the valves in the appropriate position. The position of each valve and the drenchers it controls must be clearly indicated by a wall plate. Not more than 72 drenchers may be controlled by a single controlling valve.

f. Spacing of drencher heads

Drenchers fitted on the top row below the eaves and those on the apex of the roof, must have maximum horizontal spacing of 2.5 metres. Windows or other openings, or combustible materials in walls exceeding 2.5m in width must be protected by two or more drenchers not more than 2.5m apart, and not more than 1.25m from the windows jambs. Windows separated by not more than 600mm of incombustible material may be treated as one window. Not more than 12 drenchers may be fixed on any horizontal line of pipe, and not more than six on one side of the vertical feedpipe.

g. Discharge

Drenchers may be either open or sealed. Open drenchers are operated simultaneously by the opening of the main valve, while the sealed type are individually actuated in the same way as a sprinkler head. Sealed drenchers differ little from sprinkler heads except in the shape of the deflector plate. They normally operate on the alternate system, and are more economical in the use of water than open drenchers, since only those heads operate which are required, and the pressure in consequence is maintained more efficiently.

Multiple control layouts similar to that shown in Fig. 6.2, may also be found. Although they have open heads, the main distribution pipes are charged with water or air, as the case may be, and these systems are therefore classed as 'sealed' types.

h. Drainage

All pipes and fittings above the controlling valves must be so arranged that the water can be drained away. A 20mm drain tap and pipe must be fitted immediately above each controlling valve.

In an open drencher system, the drain taps must always be kept open except when the drenchers are in operation. A full-way 50mm waste valve and pipe must also be installed below the controlling valve or valves, so that the running pressure tests can be carrried out at any time.

2   Water-spray projector systems

a. Extinction of oil fires by water

When water is used as the sole means of extinction of oil fires, it is normally applied by means of specially installed fixed fire-fighting equipment closely resembling a sprinkler system.

Precise information as to the way in which burning oil is extinguished is still incomplete, but three main factors are known to be involved (see Manual, Book 1, 'Elements of combustion and extinction)'. These are:

(i)   cooling;

(ii)   dilution of oxygen supplies, and

(iii)   Dilution (or removal) of the liquid (fuel).

(1) Cooling

Oil burns as a vapour distilling from the surface of the liquid involved in fire. Cooling the liquid reduces the rate of vapourisation and consequently the rate at which the fuel can reach the fire. When water is applied to the burning surface, the oil is cooled by contact with it, and heat absorbed by the water raises the water temperature and converts part at least into steam. The latent heat of vapourisation of water (2260 kj/kg) is such that it is of little importance whether the water projected on to the oil is hot or cold – the cooling effect is caused primarily by its conversion to steam. When water strikes the hot surface of the oil, considerable disturbance is caused and the underlying cool oil is mixed with hot oil which is thereby cooled, thus further reducing the rate of vapour formation.

(2) Dilution of oxygen supplies

The steam formed by the vapourisation of the applied water displaces air from the zone of combustion and thus tends to smother the fire. Furthermore, in water-spray projector systems, the whole of the probable fire area is surrounded by projectors, all of which come into operation at the outbreak of fire. The steam generated, together with the products of combustion seeking to escape from the fire, tend to be driven back into the zone of combustion, and thus still further reduce the oxygen available for combustion.

(3) Dilution of the liquid

If a flammable liquid which will mix with water is progressively diluted, a stage will be reached where so much water is present that the liquid will no longer burn. Petroleum oils, however, cannot mix with water but under certain conditions are capable of forming an emulsion which may consist of globules of oil suspended in water, or globules of water suspended in oil. The nature of emulsion varies widely, as does its stability; for instance, an emulsion will only last in spirit, such as petrol, whilst it is being formed, whereas in heavy oils it may take several hours to break down. The formation of an emulsion demands energy which must be provided by the water striking the surface of the oil, thus high velocity is required to give high energy to the water drops. Some of the energy may also come from the heat content of the hot oil. This, in evaporating some of the water supplied, causes turbulence which emulsifies the rest. The flammability of an oil-in-water emulsion (that is one in which the drops of oil are surrounded by water) is low because the heat from the fire must pass through the enevelope of water surrounding each drop of oil before the latter can be vapourised and add its fuel to the fire.

The relative importance of each of these three factors in the extinction of an oil fire varies considerably, but all three undoubtedly play a part in the operation of a water-spray projector system.

b. Types of system

There are two basic types of water-spray systems installed as fixed equipment. On of these is used to extinguish fires (high velocity system) and the other is used to provide protection to plant equipment and to prevent explosions (medium velocity system).

c. High velocity system

The high velocity system is used on fires involving medium and heavy oils or similar flammable liquids. This system applies water in the form of a conical spray consisting of high-velocity droplets; the three principles of extinguishment described above are employed, namely, emulsification, cooling and smothering.

(1) Projectors

The conical spray of water is discharged through specially designed high velocity projectors (Fig. 8.3). These are made in various sizes

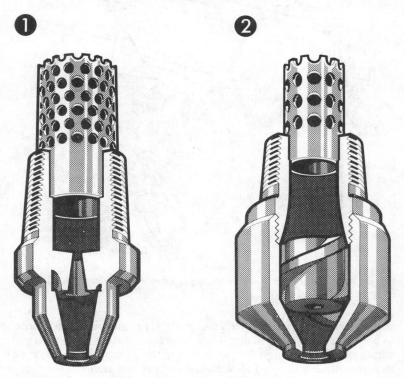

Fig. 8.3 Two types of high velocity water-spray projectors.

and are designed to give an even distribution of water over the area covered. The different sizes give a combination of differing flow rates and angles. The equipment is equally suitable for indoor or outdoor use because the pipework can be so designed that no water enters the installation until a fire is detected. The risk of water freezing in the pipework is, therefore, eliminated.

(2) Methods of operation

High velocity water-spray projector systems can be either automatic or manual in operation or, in some cases, manual only. Manual control is usually by hand-operated valves placed outside the probable fire zone, or by valves with remote control from one or more points. There are two main forms of automatic operation.

The arrangement shown in Fig. 8.4 is used in situations where fires in their incipient stages are likely to be small. Projectors are arranged in small groups to cover the risk, each group being

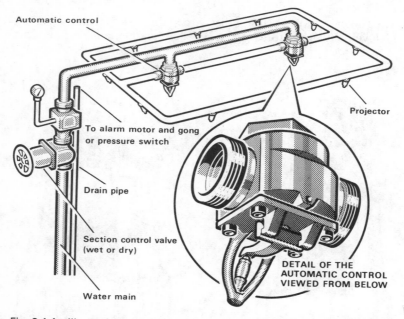

Automatic control

Projector

To alarm motor and gong or pressure switch

Drain pipe

Section control valve (wet or dry)

Water main

DETAIL OF THE AUTOMATIC CONTROL VIEWED FROM BELOW

Fig. 8.4 An illustration of a water-spray projection system and (inset) detail of an automatic control.

connected by pipework to glass-bulb type automatic controls. When fire causes a control to operate, water is discharged simultaneously through the projectors in the group. When this type of equipment is intalled in situations where the temperature may fall below freezing point, the pipework between the controlling valves and the automatic controls is charged with compressed air. Where fires are likely to be larger or to spread rapidly over an extended area, a larger number of projectors are designed to operate simultaneously. A typical application of this method of control is the deluge system illustrated in Fig. 8.5 and Plate 1. Projectors mounted on empty pipework command the whole of the exterior of the transformer and its conservation tank, and also the floor area around the transformer. Glass bulb detectors, mounted on independent pipework containing compressed air, are so positioned that wherever a fire may originate, one at least will operate and allow the compressed air in the pipework to escape. The escaping compressed air causes a rapid fall in pressure on the diaphragm in the automatic deluge valve, to which both systems of pipework are connected. The movement of the diaphragm causes the deluge valve to open and water to pass through the projectors.

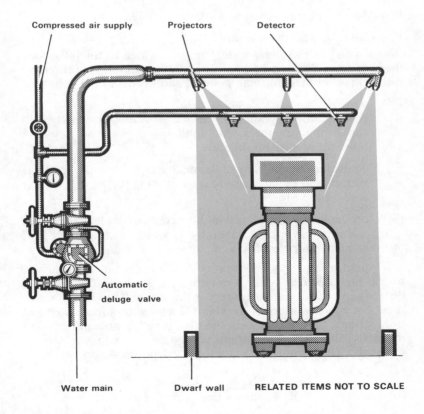

Fig. 8.5 Diagram showing the arrangement of projectors to protect an electrical transformer.

(3) Alarms

An alarm is a normal part of a water-spray projector system. It is usually of a type very similar to that used in a sprinkler system, i.e. a loud sounding gong operated by a water motor which is driven by a small flow of water diverted at the installation controlling valves when open. In addition, an electrical alarm may be provided to give warning at some control point of the outbreak of fire and its location.

(4) General

Combined high velocity systems and sprinkler protection may be used in some industrial processes which involve the use of flammable liquids. A glass bulb control forms the fire detecting element and automatic valve for a group of projectors and open sprinklers of a special type which are designed to distribute the water discharge over a wide ceiling area. When the control operates, water is discharged from the projectors on to the burning liquid and from sprinklers on to the ceiling and adjacent walls.

d. Medium velocity system

When a fire occurs, this system applies water in finely divided droplets travelling at medium velocity. It is primarily a protective rather than an extinguishing system, and produces the following effects:

(i)   cooling of the external surface of exposed vessels and supporting structures, thus inhibiting fire spread, pressure build-up or structural failure;

(ii)   controlling the burning of flammable liquids, by cooling their surface and the area above it by diluting the air and vapour feeding the fire.

(iii) producing air turbulence in the vicinity of gas leakages, thus diluting the gas and thereby reducing the possibility of combustion or explosion.

Medium velocity systems are very similar in operation and layout to the high velocity systems previously described. The sprayers discharge a cone of water spray consisting of small droplets of water with a range of different sizes and discharging angles. In most installations the system can be discharged automatically and manually, although some systems may be found which only operate manually. There are three main forms of automatic operation:

(a) the automatic control type, similar to that shown in Fig. 7.4;

(b) the deluge type, as shown in Fig. 8.5; and

(c) glass-bulb sealed sprayers, which operate individually like sprinkler heads.

3   Foam installations (LX)

There are three types of fixed foam installation and these are described below. Details of the types and properties of foam, the principles of operation of basic foam-making equipment such as inductors and generators, and the operational use of foam are given in the Manual, Book 3 Part 3: Foam and foam-making equipment.

a.   Proportional-tank mechanical foam installation

This type (Fig. 8.6) comprises a pressure vessel inside which is fitted a flexible rubber bag. The bag is filled to maximum capacity with foam concentrate. A venturi is fitted into the main water line, and a connection made from the upstream side of the venturi to the outside of the flexible rubber bag. A connection is also made from the inside of the bag to the downstream side of the venturi.

When an outlet is opened, water flows through the venturi creating a slight downstream pressure drop. The relative upstream pressure squeezes the bag and forces the foam concentrate into the main water supply downstream of the venturi. An increase in the water flow causes the downstream pressure to drop even more; this in turn allows more foam concentrate to flow into the water stream, thus maintaining the correct proportion. The resulting foam solution is fed to the appropriate foam makers or pourers in the area to be protected.

As with most foam systems, this type of installation is situated outside the area to be protected.

b.   Pump-operated foam installation

This system is illustrated in Fig. 8.7. Actuation of the system (either manually or automatically) triggers a pump, which draws foam concentrate from a simple atmospheric tank and injects it into the main water supply at a higher pressure. The flow of foam concentrate is controlled by either a metering orifice or a constant flow valve. Unlike the sytem illustrated in Fig. 8.6, this system is only suitable for a fixed flow.

c.   Pre-mixed foam installation

A pre-mixed foam installation (Fig. 8.8) comprises a cylindrical storage tank, designed for a maximum working pressure of about 10 bar, which is filled with a foam solution (i.e. foam concentrate and water). The capacity of the tank is determined by the quantity and depth of the foam coverage required. The tank is fitted with an inlet connection from a carbon dioxide gas cylinder (or cylinders) of appropriate capacity, having a disclosure valve and a lever-operated piercing head. The rate of discharge of the CO_2 gas in the event of fire is controlled so that a continuous pressure will be maintained within the storage tank, giving a constant rate of flow of foam.

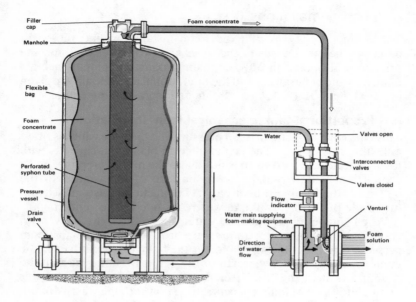

Fig. 8.6 Proportional-tank mechanical foam installation.

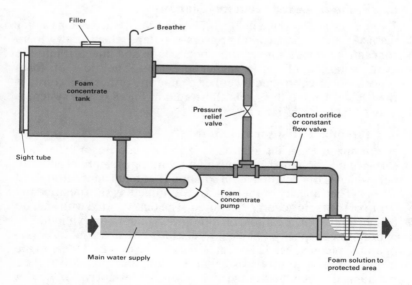

Fig. 8.7 Pump-operated foam installation.

An outbreak of fire will cause the fusible link (Fig. 8.8(1)) to break and allow the weight (2) to fall. This raises the lever of the piercing head (3) thus releasing CO_2 gas from the cylinder (4) into the storage tank (5). The foam solution (6) is forced up the siphon tube and along the outlet pipe to the foam generator (7). The foam is distributed by perforated pipes or spreaders (8) which are arranged to give even or concentrated distribution (e.g. over a boiler front) as required.

If any of the systems described in (a), (b) or (c) above protect more than one area of risk, distribution valves may be included to direct the foam to the required area.

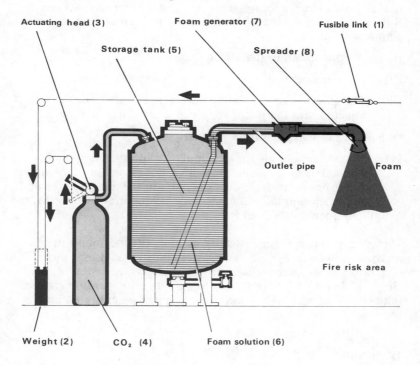

Actuating head (3)   Foam generator (7)   Fusible link (1)

Storage tank (5)   Spreader (8)

Outlet pipe   Foam

Fire risk area

Weight (2) CO_2 (4)   Foam solution (6)

Fig. 8.8 Pre-mixed foam installation.

4   High expansion foam installations (HX)

High expansion foam, as used in fixed installations, is a mass of uniform bubbles normally having an expansion ratio of between 200 and 1200 volumes of foam for each volume of solution. One of its principal attributes, therefore, is the ability to produce a large amount of foam from a small amount of water, with a consequent reduction in water damage.

In addition to the actual production of foam, high expansion foam installations can incorporate devices which automatically close fire-resisting doors and open roof vents. Such installations are electrically operated by relays from an automatic fire detector operating on the 'rate of rise of temperature' principle.

The output of an automatic high expansion foam installation will vary depending on the generator used. These are available in a wide output range, and the use of multiple generators can provide systems with a virtually unlimited output so allowing an assessment to be made of the size and number of generators required to provide adequate foam delivery in any type of building.

If any one detector locates a fire, the installation actuates and the following sequence of event is set in motion. (In practice they occur simultaneously).

(i)   Alarms sound in the affected area.

(ii) A valve opens allowing water to pass to the generator.

(iii) The pump motor is switched on and foam concentrate is injected into the water supply at a pre-determined rate.

(iv) The fan motor (if fitted) is started.

(v)   Water gathers in an accumulator, producing pneumatic pressure which opens protective doors on the generator, opens doors covering duct openings in the affected area and sets in motion the mechanism for closing fire-resisting doors and opening roof vents.

High-expansion foam installations may also be found in open areas, as shown in Plate 6. The system illustrated uses a series of generators powered by water turbine as described in the Manual, Book 3 Chapter 10. It produces foam with an expansion ratio of between 400:1 and 700:1, and operation can be either manual or automatic.

5   Foam inlets

In many buildings rooms containing oil or other flammable liquids are protected by fixed piping through which foam can be pumped. The piping is run from the room to an appropriate point in the street where it terminates in a fire service inlet (Fig. 8.9) usually protected by a glass panel and marked with the words FOAM INLET, together with an indication of the particular risk involved.

The inlet pipes are fitted with a foam inlet adaptor, a specification for which is included in BS 336 (1980). This has a tapered orifice against which the foam making branch is held by hand. The orifice is suitable for most types of low expansion (foam-making) branch.

This arrangement ensures that foam can be applied where it is required in the early stages of what may be a fierce fire without it being necessary for firefighters to enter the compartment.

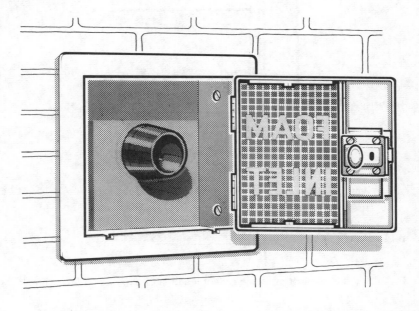

Fig. 8.9 A Fire Service foam inlet, tapered type in accordance with BS 336.

6 Rising mains

A rising main (Fig. 8.10) consists essentially of a pipe installed vertically in a building with a fire service inlet or town main connection at the lower end and outlets at various levels throughout the building.

In some buildings a system of internal private hydrants is fitted and whilst this system is not strictly speaking a rising main, it operates on similar principles and for all practical purposes may be treated as being the same.

The outlet valves of these hydrants are usually sealed with a wire and lead seal by the water authority to prevent them from being used for purposes other than fire fighting. The outlets are mostly of the wheel-operated type opening anti-clockwise; the direction of

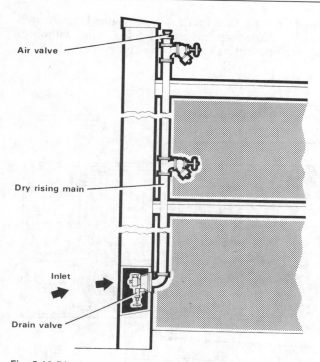

Fig. 8.10 Diagram illustrating the salient features of a dry-rising fire main.

opening, however, is always indicated either on the wheel itself or on a plate fitted between the wheel and the locking nut.

Hose may be provided by the occupier for use with risers or internal hydrants, but the modern tendency is to provide a small diameter hose reel which is more manageable by untrained persons making an initial attack on a fire.

There are two types of rising main.

(a) wet risers;

(b) dry risers.

a. Wet risers

A wet riser is a pipe kept permanently charged with water which is then immediately available for use on any floor at which a hydrant outlet (sometimes known as a landing valve) is provided. The riser is connected to a town main of suitable capacity with a shut-off control valve installed. If the building height is such that the pressure in the main is insufficient to supply four 13mm jets at 2.5 bar at the highest outlet, booster pumps are necessary at suitable levels to ensure the maintenance of the required pressure and flow.

Where these pumps are employed, the landing valves must be fitted with a pressure regulator to ensure that the pressure head against the pumps (which can be in excess of 20 bar), is not transmitted to the hose.

A similar function to that of a wet riser is performed by what is known as a 'down-comer'. This, like a wet riser, is constructed of vertical piping, but is supplied with water from a tank in the roof or at intermediate levels.

b. Dry risers

A dry riser is simply a vertical pipe which is normally kept empty of water, fitted with outlets at various floor levels in the building. It is not connected to a water supply, but is charged when required by means of fire service pumps. In effect, it is a substitute for a line of hose, over which it has many advantages. It enables an upper floor level fire to be attacked by the fire brigade with a line of standard hose without the loss of time entailed in having to lay hose up through the building from the street. It also has a considerably greater capacity than 70mm hose and obviates the risk of water damage which might occur if a hose line burst in a part of the building not affected by fire. Further, since an outlet at or near roof level is invariably provided, a riser can be used to feed branches covering a fire in an adjacent building.

A dry riser is charged through inlets at ground level, which are usually housed in external glass-fronted boxes. Each box is normally identified by the words DRY RISER painted in red on the glass. Inlets may occasionally be found below pavement level in a box with a cover similar to that used for a hydrant..

An air valve is sometimes fitted at the highest point in the pipe (see Fig. 8.10) to allow contained air to discharge to atmosphere when the riser is charged with water. Without such a provision, air in the riser might be compressed in the upper part of the pipe and prevent it being fully charged. The air valve, if fitted, is constructed to admit air to the pipe where it is drained after use and so prevent the creation of the partial vacuum, which would result in pockets of water being trapped.

Dry risers are provided with a drain cock fitted beneath the inlets to enable the system to be drained after use. Additionally, where an outlet is fixed at a position below the inlet valves, a further drain valve is fitted at the lowest point of the riser. When emptying a dry riser, it is advisable, if no automatic air valve is fitted, to open the highest outlet to admit air.

c. Type to be used

The type of rising main to be installed in a building is generally determined by the height of the building. In buildings over 18 metres in height, it is recommended that a dry rising fire main be installed, and in those above 60 metres, a wet riser is necessary. As mentioned earlier, booster pumps will be required and a storage tank of about 45m^3 capacity will be needed with a wet riser. The reason why a wet riser must be provided above 60 metres is that brigade pumps will not supply the necessary quantity of water pressure above this height. For operational reasons, however, the fire service may require dry or wet risers at levels lower than those quoted above.

The outlets from risers should be found in a firefighting staircase lobby, in an enclosed staircase forming part of an exit, or in a fire enclosure. They may be placed in a glazed cupboard, clearly marked in accordance with BS 5499 Part 1.

Brigades should devise their own plans to overcome the problem of theft of wheel valves and other removable parts of outlets which, if not anticipated, will render the riser unserviceable in the event of a fire. Further, where a dry riser is installed, the possibility of vandalism may make it necessary to check that the wheel valves on each floor are in fact turned off before charging the riser at the inlet. Various methods are being tried in buildings to disguise and/or protect riser outlets from vandals. It is important therefore that the fire brigade is familiar with the siting of, and access to, rising main outlets in buildings within its area

7 Hose reels

Increasing use is being made of hydraulic hose reels (Fig.8.11) the first line of attack in buildings today. The comparative lightness and lack of jet reaction from the nozzle makes the hose reel a suitable

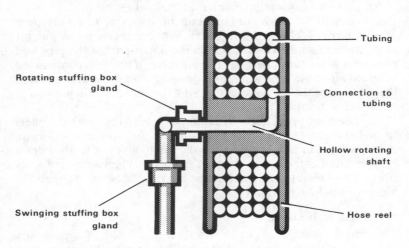

Fig. 8.11 Cross-sectional drawing of a typical hydraulic hose reel.

item of equipment for the public. Since only the amount of tubing required needs to be pulled off the reel before the water is turned on (in some cases the water can be turned on before any tubing is run out) only one person is needed to operate it. So many different types of hose reel are in use that it is impractical to describe every variation. In principal, however, the equipment is very similar to the standard hose reel fitted to fire appliances, and no difficulty should be experienced in using any type found.

a. Connections

A connection is made to the nearest water supply, which may be a wet riser or some kind of internal hydrant system. A stop valve is fitted to control the supply of water to the hose reel, which is usually charged to the nozzle before this valve is closed. The reel itself is mounted on a hollow rotating shaft, to the centre of which is fed through a stuffing box gland, the tubing being connected to an outlet on this rotating shaft. Rubber tubing of 20 or 25mm in diameter is employed and a light branch with a shut-off nozzle is fitted.

b. Operation

To operate this type of hose reel, all that is necessary is to turn on the valve, and holding the branch, pull off as much tubing as necessary from the reel; the shut-off nozzle is opened when the fire is reached. On some types an automatic valve is fitted to obviate serious delay should the operator fail to turn on the valve before taking the branch to the fire. In one type the action of removing the branch from its holder opens the valve; in another the valve is automatically turned on by the rotation of the drum after a few turns of tubing have been pulled off. To ensure that the tubing pays out easily without kinking or fouling, some form of metal guide is provided, or alternatively, the whole reel swings in the direction in which the tubing is being unreeled. Hose reels are sometimes provided with a fixed metal cover to prevent the collection of dust and to protect the rubber tubing from exposure to light which in time causes deterioration of the rubber.

8   Private hydrants

Private hydrants are often installed in premises with extensive yards, sidings, storage areas, etc. where the nearest statutory hydrant is a considerable distance from the risk, or where the nature of the risk requires large quantities of water to be immediately to hand.

a. Connections

These hydrants may be connected to the service main to the premises, if this is of large enough capacity, to a separate branch from the town main, to a ring main which is connected to the town main at two points or, occasionally, by a single connection.

Ring mains are also installed without any connection to town mains, being supplied from private water supplies such as overhead tanks, reservoirs, lakes, canals, etc. Some premises with a supply from lakes, canals, etc. may also use the town main as a supplementary or primary supply in a fire situation. In this event, the arrangement of valves in the system must ensure that there can be no possibility of contamination of the town main.

A ring main installation has many obvious advantages, the most important of which is that any hydrant is fed by both arms of the ring and that, since a division valve is fitted in both connections with the town main or other water supply and, sometimes, at intermediate points, it may be possible to isolate a damaged section and thus allow a portion of the ring to remain in action. Where premises are equipped with a sprinkler system as well as private hydrants, separate branches should be provided for each.

b. Hydrant markings

Increasing use is being made of standard hydrant indicator plates (see the Manual, Book 7, Hydraulics, pumps and pump operation) to mark the position of private hydrants, although various individual markings may still be found. The hydrants themselves are of various patterns, the most common being the standard underground hydrant; less common are pillar hydrants and wall hydrants.

c. Outlets

The outlets of private hydrants usually conform to British Standard 750, although other types may be found. Where private hydrants are non-standard, adaptors should be provided at the premises to enable fire brigade equipment to be used.

d. By-pass valves

As private mains usually supply the domestic needs of the premises, they are almost always fitted with a water meter so that the water undertakings can record a consumption. Where water is fed into industrial premises for business purposes through a meter, it is common practice for a by-pass to be fitted. If water on the factory side of the meter is required for fire fighting, the meter can be by-passed by opening the by-pass valve, thus eliminating frictional resistance through the meter. In addition, the waste used for fire fighting does not register on the meter. The location of the valve controlling a meter by-pass should be indicated by a standard by-pass indicator plate (see the Manual, Book 7). The valve is usually wire-locked in the closed position and when a hydrant is used for fire fighting, the valve should be opened fully to enable the maximum flow to be obtained.

Chapter 9
Extinguishing systems not using water

This chapter deals with the equipment and fittings installed to protect buildings by means other than the use of water. A firefighter needs to be familiar with the types of media used in the installations. They include carbon dioxide and halon systems with a brief mention of powder and inert gas equipment.

1 Carbon Dioxide installations

a. Applications and limitations of carbon dioxide

The use of carbon dioxide installation is confined primarily to hazards which are located inside buildings, or around which protective screens can be erected. Although heavier than air, the gas may be dispersed away from the fire if subjected to any appreciable currents of air. The gas discharges at low temperature, but this does not produce much cooling effect in the fire area and is never taken into consideration when designing an installation, dilution of the atmosphere being the main extinguishing effect.

Carbon dioxide is not suitable for extinguishing fires involving materials which contain their own oxygen supply, e.g. nitrates, chlorates or reactive metals such as sodium, potassium, magnesium, etc. It has a particular application where delicate equipment or materials are involved and some examples of the type of risk where it can be used satisfactorily are:

(i) a wide variety of electrical apparatus and electronic equipment, e.g. electrical switch gear, transformers, alternators, computers, telephone relays and repeater stations.

(ii) flammable liquids e.g. paint store, paint dip tanks, small spray booths, solvent stores, printing ink;

(iii) chemical laboratories and chemical stores (depending on the type of chemicals involved).

(iv) libraries, archives, valuable art stores, record stores etc.

(v) diesel and diesel-electric locomotives, ships' holds, machinery in textile industry.

b. Gas stored in cylinders

An installation consists of a battery of one or more cylinders of carbon dioxide interconnected by a manifold and feeding into a system of high-pressure distribution pipework. Special discharge nozzles are fitted at intervals on the pipework and upon operation of the installation, the gas is discharged, with considerable noise, into the protected space or on to the particular hazard. Operation of the installation can be either automatic, or manual, by the use of electrical or mechanical equipment (see Fig. 9.1 and Plate 7).

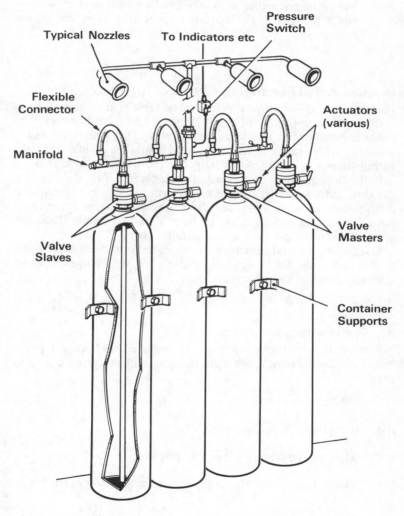

Fig. 9.1 A battery of CO_2 cylinders covering a small risk.

Where protection is required for more than one compartment or zone, one of the following arrangements is usually found:

(i)   sufficient cylinders may be provided to flood all spaces simultaneously;

(ii)   a separate group of cylinders may be provided for each space, in which case they can be interconnected and used as reserves;

(iii)   one battery of cylinders may be used with adjustable valves to direct the gas to the required space (this is termed 'joint protection').

c.   Gas stored in refrigerated tanks

Here the gas is stored in a refrigerated tank at a temperature of $-18°C$ and at a pressure of about 20 bar. The tank is connected by suitable pipework to the discharge nozzles in the protected space. Tank capacities range from 3 tonne and a number of different risks within the same premises can be protected using a single tank.

Operation of the system is usually triggered off by the use of a suitable automatic fire detection system. When it operates, a distribution valve is automatically opened for a predetermined period, allowing sufficient gas to be released to totally flood the protected space, and then automatically closes.

Overriding manual control is incorporated into the design of the system and, should re-ignition occur, further charges can be released into the space as required.

d.   General considerations

When considering how much gas is required and what type of installation is necessary, the main factors which are given attention are:

(i)   the volume of space;

(ii)   the nature of the hazard;

(iii)   whether the hazard is enclosed or not;

(iv)   whether fire is likely to spread from one compartment to another;

(v)   the chances of fire recurring in more than one space at a time.

Plate 1. A typical emulsified water projection system in operation.

Plate 2. An example of a butterfly sprinkler valve group.
Photo. Wormald.

Plate 3. Three sprinkler heads, one bulb and two fusible solder.
Photo. Building Research Establishment.

Plate 4. A sprinkler head operating.
Photo. Building Research Establishment.

Plate 5. Gem fast-response sprinkler head.
Photo. Kidde General Fire Ltd.

Plate 6. A typical HX foam application system in operation.

Plate 7. An example of a small local application CO_2
system.
Photo. Chubb Fire.

Plate 8. Ionisation smoke detector.
Photo. Chubb Fire.

Plate 9. Optical smoke detector.
Photo. Chubb Fire.

Plate 10. Infra-red scanning radiation detector.
Photo. Thorn Security Ltd.

Plate 11. Fixed temperature heat detector.
Photo. Chubb Fire.

Plate 12. Rate of rise heat detector.
Photo. Chubb Fire.

Plate 13. Rate of rise heat detector, pneumatic type.
Photo. Kidde General Fire Ltd.

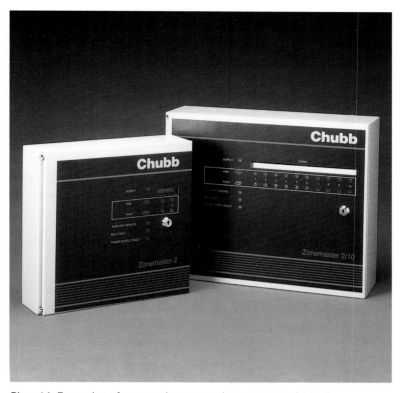

Plate 14. Examples of two- and ten-zone detector control panels.
Photo. Chubb Fire.

Plate 15. Detector control panel showing a pre-alarm signal, displayed message and printout.
Photo. Kidde General Fire Ltd.

Plate 16. Manual fire alarm showing microprocessor which can be fitted to include the alarm into an analogue system.
Photo. Apollo Fire Detectors Ltd.

Plate 17. Entrance to a shopping mall. All the perimeter windows are vertical casement automatic ventilators.
Photo. Colt International Ltd.

Plate 18. Louvred fire and smoke automatic ventilators fitted into a typical long mall.
Photo. Colt International Ltd.

Plate 19. Similar louvred ventilators, to those in Plate 18, fitted to a flat roof.
Photo. Colt International Ltd.

Plate 20. Powered heat and smoke ventilators either manually or automatically controlled.
Photo. Colt International Ltd.

Plate 21. Part of shopping mall with smoke curtains/dams retracted.

Plate 22. As Plate 21 with curtains/dams operated.

Plate 23. Another example of a shopping mall showing vertical and roof ventilators.
Photo. Colt International Ltd.

Plate 24. Typical metal ducting being fitted into a shopping mall.
Photo. Capital and Counties Ltd.

e. Lock-off devices

Every installation must be provided with means of immobilising the equipment, as it is important that automatic operation should not occur whilst people are in the protected zone. Provision is usually made to:

(i)   'lock-off' the automatic feature only (leaving over-riding manual control), and

(ii)   completely immobilise the installation.

These devices can usually be operated from a remote position outside the protected area.

f. Indicating and alarm devices

Automatic visual warning, using a system of coloured indicator lights, is usually provided to indicate:

(i)   manual control;

(ii)   automatic control;

(iii) carbon dioxide discharged.

In addition, visible and/or audible warning may be provided to indicate an electrical fault. All indicators may terminate at a central control where necessary, in addition to a warning on site.

g. Other automatic devices

By diverting a small amount of gas to pressure-operated switches and trip mechanisms it is possible automatically to:

(i)   operate door-closing devices;

(ii)   close openings in ventilating ducts;

(iii) switch off ventilating systems;

(iv)   operate fire curtains.

h. General safety precautions

Aisles and routes of exits should be kept clear at all times. Adequate lighting and/or emergency lighting with directional signs to ensure quick staff evacuation may be necessary for large protected chambers. Sufficient alarms should be provided within the area to operate immediately upon detection of fire and at the time of CO_2 discharge. Alternatively, the alarms should sound for a timed interval before operation of the CO_2 installation. Automatic closure of doors should not prevent the doors being re-opened by trapped personnel. Outward-swinging self-closing doors are recommended.

Warning and instructional signs or notices should be positioned at the entrance to protected fire risks. In most cases where CO_2 is installed, the actual hazard to personnel is rather small, but the hazard will always be greater where the enclosure is large and where carbon dioxide may enter adjacent spaces such as pits and basements.

The extent and type of warning must be designed to suit the particular site but it should always include the symbol shown in Fig. 9.2. Usually adequate warning notices, bells and indicating lights are provided with an installation for the guidance of staff and it is recommended that firefighters should comply with the instructions given on such notices.

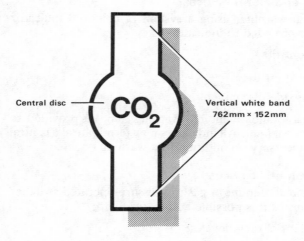

Fig. 9.2 Standard CO_2 warning symbol.

Instruction and drills should be carried out to ensure that correct action is taken by staff when the equipment operates. Provision should be made for the prompt ventilation of areas into which CO_2 has been discharged. The hazardous atmosphere should be dissipated and not merely transferred to another area.

i.   Action by the Fire Service

Most of the advice given in section 2(c) below in respect of total-flooding type halon systems is equally applicable to CO_2 installations. It should be noted however that CO_2 is generally less quick at extinguishing a fire. Also, unlike halons, it does not decompose, but the gas itself, and the products of combustion, will still be a potential hazard.

2 Halon installations

a. General

Halons (halogenated hydrocarbons) are described in the Manual, Book 3 Chapter 6. The following three may be found in fixed installations:

(i)   bromotrifluoromethane (generally referred to as halon 1301 or BTM);

(ii)   bromochlorodifluoromethane (generally referred to as halon 1211 or BCF);

(iii)   chlorobromomethane (generally referred to as halon 1011 or CBM) (this has largely been superseded by BTM and BCF).

These extinguishants have the same cleanliness in operation as carbon dioxide, are more efficient but more expensive.

Halons should not be used to extinguish fires involving chemicals containing their own oxygen supply, or metal hydrides.

b. Principles of operation

Halons are stored under pressure in liquid form and are designed to vaporise quickly when released in the fire zone. It is usual to pressurise their containers with nitrogen to ensure efficient discharge.

Each container in a fixed halon installation is equipped with suitably designed valves to retain the agent in the container and discharge it at the required rate when necessary. Containers with top-mounted valves have an internal dip tube extending to the bottom of the cylinder to permit discharge of the liquid. When the system operates, the liquid is fed through distribution pipework to specially-designed discharge nozzles which are sited strategically round the risk. Upon discharge the liquid vaporises to form a heavy vapour which achieves very rapid extinction.

Because of their high efficiency halons are ideally suitable for use in automatic systems, and these should be used in preference to manual operation. The inevitable delay involved in the actuation of a manual system may reduce its effectiveness, because the size of the fire may be increased and this could result in an increase in the concentration of toxic breakdown products when the halon is eventually discharged. However, in some circumstances manual operation will be necessary for safety reasons (see below).

c. Types of system

There are two types of system which may be found installed:

(i)   total flooding systems;

(ii)   local application systems.

A total flooding system consists of a supply of the halon arranged to discharge into and fill to the required concentration, an enclosed space about the hazard. This system is very similar in layout to the carbon dioxide system and may provide fire protection within rooms, vaults, enclosed machines, ovens, containers, storage tanks and bins.

Local application systems may be used to extinguish surface fires in flammable liquids, gases and solids where the hazard is not enclosed. Hazards that may be successfully protected include dip tanks, quench tanks, spray booths and oil-filled electric transformers.

In total flooding systems, the high density of Halon 1301 vapour (five times that of air) requires the use of discharge nozzles that will achieve a well-mixed atmosphere in order to avoid pockets of higher concentration. It is also possible to develop such pockets in low-lying areas adjacent to local application systems. Once mixed into the air, the agent will not settle out. It is always advisable to back up any system, whether of local application or total flooding, with suitable media in case the system fails to function.

d. Safety precautions

Similar general safety precautions to those for CO_2 installations should be adopted in the case of halon systems. Total flooding systems should be set to manual control or completely immobilised, whilst people are present in the protected area, except where a Halon 1301 system is designed to give a concentration of 6 per cent or less. In this case, short term exposure to the agent is unlikely to have any harmful effects; nevertheless, evacuation should still be undertaken without delay.

Discharge of the agent may be detectable by a light mist in the vicinity of the discharge nozzle, resulting from condensation of moisture in the air, but the mist rarely persists after discharge is completed. Once discharged into an enclosure, it is difficult to detect its presence through normal human senses; in high concentrations, however, voice characteristics are changed due to the increased density of the agent/air mixture.

3 Powder installations

Powder provides a further range of chemical agents available as extinguishing media, and the properties of these are dealt with in the Manual, Book 3 Chapter 5. In common with halons, powders offer the advantage of a quick knock-down of fire, but unlike halons, they have negligible toxic effects. A major disadvantage is that they require a lot of clearing up once an installation has operated. Compacting of the powder is also a problem, due to heat or vibration in normal storage and in moist atmospheres; this could present difficulties in the maintenance of the system, especially after discharge when compacting could take place in valves, etc. The more recently developed powders however, do not have this problem.

A dry powder installation consists of specially-designed pipework and discharge nozzles covering the protected risk, the pipework being linked to the powder containers. When a fire occurs it is necessary to exert pressure on the powder so that it is forced through the pipework and discharge nozzles. This is usually done with CO_2; a line detector is linked to a lever which when actuated allows the head of a CO_2 cylinder to be pierced (similar to the operation shown in Fig. 8.8). The carbon dioxide thus released ejects the powder. Powder installations can normally be operated automatically or manually.

Powder can be used on various flammable liquids, flammable gases, oil-filled equipment and in the case of general combustible solids where the fire is on the surface. Special powders have been developed to deal with metal fires (see Manual, Part 6C, Practical Firemanship III, Chapter 45 Section 7 'Metal Fires').

4 Inert gas installations

Several inert gas systems using the combustion products of diesel oil have been developed. These systems can generate large amounts of gas (mostly nitrogen) so that whilst a fire is being dealt with in one particular space, the gas can also be directed to adjacent spaces to stop it spreading. Alternatively, spaces can be kept permanently filled with inert gas as a precaution against an outbreak of fire.

The use of this type of installation is mainly confined to the protection of ships' holds and is described in detail in the Manual, Book 4, Part 2 'Incidents involving shipping'.

Part 2
Fire alarm systems

A general alarm of fire in a building can be raised either by a person actuating a manual fire alarm or automatically, by a detection system.

Even when a building is occupied, an automatic detection system offers advantages over a manual system in those areas which are remote, secured, seldom visited etc. and where fires can start, take hold and cause damage before they are discovered. At the times when buildings are not occupied, the advantages of early detection are obvious.

The Loss Prevention Council (LPC) issues rules detailing their requirements for the installation, testing and maintenance of efficient automatic detection systems and offer subtantial cuts in insurance premiums as incentives towards their installation.

The design and installation of electrical fire alarm systems are also covered by BS 3116 Part 4 and BS 5839 Part 1.

This part of the book examines the principles of the various types of fire alarm systems, gives examples and discusses the siting of them.

Chapter 10
Automatic fire detection

1 Principles of automatic fire detection

The function of fire detectors is to detect one or more changes in the protected environment indicating the development of a fire condition. They may operate:

(i)   When the invisible products of combustion are being released;

(ii) When smoke is being produced:

(iii) When the temperature in the vicinity of the fire rises rapidly or reaches a pre-determined figure.

The types of detector designed to operate at these respective stages are:–

(a) Ionisation
(b) Optical   } smoke detectors
(c) Radiation
(d) Heat

The choice of type of detector system has to be based on the type of risk to be protected, the circumstances surrounding that risk, reliability, robustness and lastly, economics (Fig. 10.1)

2 Types of system

Systems may be installed in buildings for:

(i)   the protection of life;

(ii) the protection of property;

(iii) a mixture of these purposes, either simultaneously or at different times and places.

BS 5939 'Fire Detection and Alarm Systems for Buildings': Part 1 'Installation and Servicing' divides systems into a number of different types, each identified by a letter and a number.

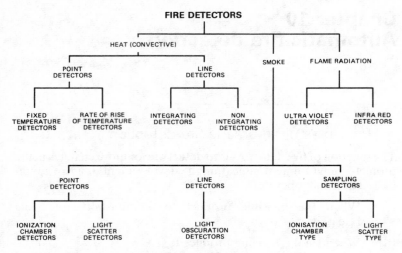

Fig. 10.1 Types of detector systems.

Type L systems are automatic detection systems intended for the protection of Life and are sub-divided into:–

Type L1 systems installed throughout the building.

L2 systems installed only in defined parts of the building. This type of system should normally include the coverage required of a 'Type L3' system.

L3 systems installed only for the protection of escape routes.

Type P systems are automatic detection systems intended to protect property and are sub-divided into:–

Type P1 systems installed throughout the protected building.

P2 systems installed only in defined parts of the pro-tected building.

Type M systems are manual alarm systems (see Chapter 18). This category has no sub-divisions.

3   Definition of a detector

The British Standard 5839 Pt 1 states a definition of a detector:

A part of an automatic fire detection system that contains at least one sensor which constantly, or at frequent intervals, monitors at least one suitable physical and/or chemical phenomenon associated with fire. It provides at least one corresponding signal to the control and indicating equipment. The decision to give the alarm of fire, or to operate automatic fire protection equipment, may be made at the detector or at another part of the system, e.g. at the control and indicating equipment.

4 Classification of detectors

(i)   Analogue detector:
A detector which gives an output signal representing the value of the sensed phenomena. This may be a true analogue signal or digitally coded equivalent of the sensed value. The detector does not itself make a decision of fire; this is done by the control equipment to which the signal is passed.

(ii)   Multi-state detector:
        A detector which gives one of a limited number (greater than two) of output states relating to 'normal' or 'fire alarm' or other abnormal conditions.

(iii)   Two-state detector:
        A detector which gives one of two output states relating to either 'normal' or 'fire alarm' conditions.

5 Success or failure of operation

When a fire occurs in an area protected by an AFD, the probable sequence of events is as depicted in Fig. 10.2. After ignition, the fire will grow, probably slowly and irregularly at first, but then at an accelerating rate.

Generally products of the fire will be transported to the detector and they will be 'checked' against the prevailing environment. When the detection system is sufficiently 'sure' that what it is detecting is not an 'environmental fluctuation' it will 'decide' that a fire exists and raise the alarm. All this appears straightforward but there are many ways in which an AFD system could fail. For example:

(i)   Wind or draught fluctuations causing a false temperature reading.

(ii)   Obstructions to smoke travel, heat or flame radiation preventing the detector from acting quickly enough.

(iii)   The detector may be unable to detect the products of that particular fire.

(iv)   A fault in the system may have made the detector inoperative.

(v)   The system may be switched off for servicing (more strictly a maintenance system failure).

(vi) The detector may be prone to false alarms, so that a genuine alarm may be ignored until a late investigation is made.

(vii) In certain areas at certain times insects may trigger false alarms

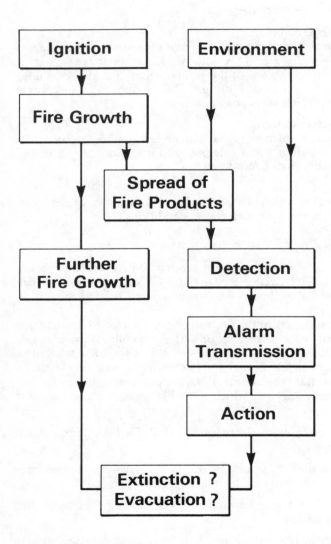

Fig. 10.2 Probable sequence of events leading to automatic detection.

6   Fire products

a.   Types of products

Products from fire will travel either by radiation or by physical
movement of the atmosphere. Radiation is fast-moving in straight
lines, physical movement is slower but more flexible. A broad term
used for physical transport is 'mass transport' and it is by this that
most smoke and heat detectors work. Flame detectors use
radiation.

b.   Mass transport

The effect of mass transport will generally depend on the height of
the ceiling from the floor, or level where the fire occurs. For
example, taking a fire at floor level in a 2.5m high room, to obtain a
ceiling temperature of 65°C from an ambient temperature of 20°C,
requires a heat output of 22.5kW. In a 10m high room it will require
720kW. It is obvious that, for the same type of detector in each case,
it will take a much larger fire to operate it in a 10m room than in a
2.5m room

Other factors are also relevant. It is well known that if a plume of
smoke and gases from a fire reaches a horizontal ceiling, it will stop
rising and spread radially outwards under the ceiling (Fig. 10.3). If

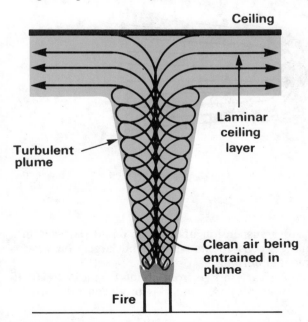

Fig. 10.3 Probable movement of smoke and gases on reaching on
horizontal ceiling.

the ceiling is sloping it will spread up the slope but there will be little movement down the slope (Fig. 10.4). As they rise, the gases will begin to cool, and, with a small fire, if there is already a heated layer of air at, or near, ceiling level, e.g. solar heating of a roof, the plume may not even reach the ceiling.

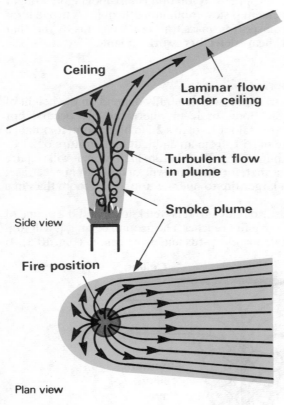

Ceiling

Laminar flow under ceiling

Turbulent flow in plume

Smoke plume

Side view

Fire position

Plan view

Fig. 10.4 Probable flow of smoke and gases on reaching a sloping ceiling.

c. Smoke

Smoke consists of a suspension of solid or liquid particles in a gaseous medium. Its constituents will depend largely on what is burning and how it is burning.

Particles in smoke vary in size from about 1 nanometre to 10 micrometres (see footnote). As smoke is produced the particles

FOOTNOTE: (A micrometre is one millionth of a metre and a nanometre is one thousandth of a micrometre).

coagulate into larger and larger solids until, eventually, they could precipitate out. The process of coagulation depends on the source and speed of the combustion. Slow-burning fires tend to produce larger particles and this, in itself, can have a significance in the choice of detector for a particular risk.

The optical properties of a particle will affect light by absorption or refraction. Depending on its constituents, smoke can appear almost white or any shade from that to sooty black. These effects are due to how much light is being absorbed or 'scattered' by the particles. This is another aspect which will affect the choice of detector.

d. Radiation

All objects give off thermal radiation. As the temperature of an object increases, the radiation it emits increases in intensity and changes colour (from red heat to white heat). Flames also emit radiation, the wavelengths depending on what is burning and how much oxygen is available. Certain wavelengths are characteristic of certain materials, e.g. a town-gas flame is transparent and dark blue.

These wavelengths, however, can be absorbed by background interference, either natural or man-made. A major natural interference source is, of course, the sun. Infra-red radiation from the sun is, generally, more powerful than infra-red from a fire, so special design has to be incorporated in flame detectors to account for solar radiation. The usual method is to design the detector to detect flame flicker, This, however, can be simulated by sunlight through the moving branches of a tree, reflection from water surfaces etc, and, where this can happen, it must be modulated out. Man-made interference may come from welding or tungsten lamps and thought must be given to these sources of false alarms.

Ultra-violet radiation is also given off by a fire, and again one natural source of UV radiation is the sun. However, the ozone layer does filter out a certain band of UV wavelengths and it is this band that can be used by detectors if they are not designed specifically to combat UV radiation.

Another source of natural UV radiation is lightning but this is of such brief duration that detectors are easily able to disregard it. Again, welding and tungsten lamps are examples of man-made UV radiation and the same precautions need to be taken as for infra-red.

Any flame detector needs to 'see' its protection area clearly because, as stated before, radiation travels in straight lines. Any obstruction, however temporary, could severely limit a detector's capability.

e. Heat

Heat is transmitted in three ways: conduction, convection and radiation (see *Manual* Book 1). Heat detectors rely primarily on convection.

The amount of heat produced by a fire depends on the source and speed of combustion, whilst the speed at which it is transmitted to the detector will depend on the ambient conditions. This latter factor is a particularly important consideration in choosing the most suitable detector (see Chapter 13 Section 5). The size and shape of the room, or space, will also need to be taken into account (see (b) above).

Since heat, generally, takes longer to evolve in significant quantities than either smoke or radiation, it should not be used as the sole basis for fire detection in situations which demand a high speed response e.g. where there is a life risk.

7 Conclusion

It can be seen from the foregoing that the correct choice and siting of detectors for the particular risk is essential. This part describes some of the various systems used. It examines the principles of the three main types, i.e. smoke, heat and radiation, and describes how these principles are applied to examples of the many current models available.

Chapter 11
Smoke detectors

1 Ionisation detector

a. The theory

What is 'ionisation'? An atom is made up of protons, electrons and neutrons, the protons and electrons being in balance as shown below (three of each in this case) (see Fig. 11.1).

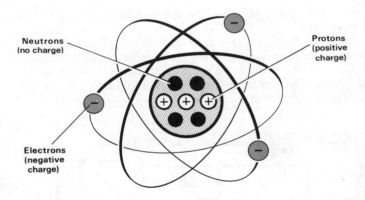

Fig. 11.1 Diagram of an atom

If the atom is subjected to radiation from a radioactive source some electrons become detached. As a result the atom becomes positively charged (i.e. it has more protons than electrons); the 'free' electrons quickly link up with other atoms which become negatively charged (i.e. more electrons than protons). These 'new' atoms are called 'ions' and the process that creates them is called 'ionisation' (Fig. 11.2).

If the atoms of air in a container are subjected to radiation, ionisation will take place in this way, and the ions will move about haphazardly. If we then introduce a positively-charged plate and a negatively-charged plate to the container a more orderly and predictable movement of ions will take place; the positive ions are

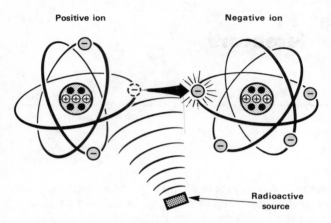

Fig. 11.2 Process of ionisation.

attracted to the negative plate and the negative ions are attracted to the positive plate.

This forms the basis of the ionisation detector (Fig. 11.3).

The movement of ions between the plates in the chamber reduces the resistance of the air so that a small electric current flows in the external circuit. The current is small and is amplified so that it can be readily monitored.

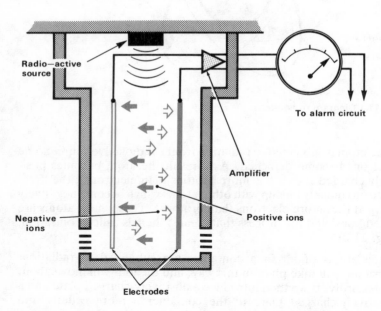

Fig. 11.3 Diagram of an ionisation detector (non-fire condition).

100

In a fire condition (Fig. 11.4) smoke particles entering the chamber become attached to the ions because of electrostatic attraction and slow their movement. This causes a reduction in the current flow. When the current falls below a predetermined level the amplifier senses it and initiates an alarm. That is the basic concept of the ionisation detector – in practice it is a little more sophisticated as can be seen from the following paragraphs.

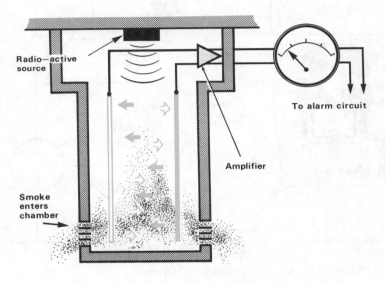

Fig. 11.4 Diagram of an ionisation detector (fire condition).

b. The practice

An illustration of one type of double chamber ionisation detector is shown in Fig. 11.5 (see also Plate 8). One ionisation chamber is in a semi-sealed environment which does not permit the entry of smoke, the other is open to the atmosphere and therefore permits smoke to enter.

In normal conditions both the inner and open chambers will be free from smoke and form a balanced electrical circuit. In a 'non-fire' condition the voltage at (1) is sufficient to fire the cold cathode tube (2) which acts as a switch controlling the operation of the relay. When smoke enters the chamber, however, it will slow the movement of ions as described earlier. As the movement of ions is slowed only in the open chamber this effectively unbalances the electrical circuit – in simple terms the open chamber now offers a higher resistance to the flow of electricity than the inner chamber does. This increases the voltage at (1) and causes the cold cathode tube to 'strike' thus forming a high current path to operate the relay and hence sound the alarm.

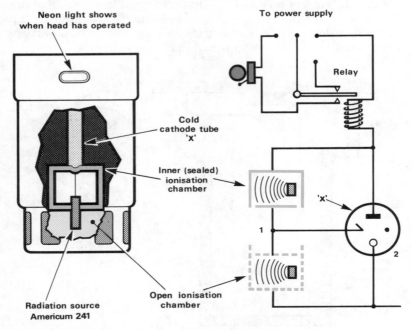

Fig. 11.5 Diagram of one type of ionisation detector.

Although this example, for ease of illustration, shows a cold cathode tube as the amplifier and 'switch mechanism', solid state amplifiers (using transistors etc.) are used to perform this function in many ionisation detectors.

An advantage of the ionisation detector is its sensitivity in the early stages of fire when smoke particles are small. Because of this sensitivity care must be taken in the siting of the detector heads. In some locations such as a garage or kitchen the products of combustion could be present in 'non-fire' conditions. Siting ionisation detectors in these areas could result in repeated false alarms.

It is particularly important that the detectors are not placed near a ventilator or fresh air inlet where a current of clean air can pass over them and inhibit their speed of reaction in a fire situation.

Most types of ionisation detector head are designed to be mounted on the ceiling and usually provide adequate coverage for 100 square metres of floor area. With slight modifications they can be fitted in air ducts for air-cooled machinery and thus give early warning of possible fire damage to intricate and expensive equipment.

Ionisation detectors with single chambers have been produced using a capacitor as a replacement for the second (inner) chamber. They have not been widely used however and the two-chamber type described above is the one most commonly found.

The radioactive source used in most ionisation-type detectors is Americium 241 which emits alpha particles and low-energy gamma rays. It has been proved that these sources present no danger to people even when damaged by fire.

2 Optical detector

While the ionisation detector responds to the invisible products of combustion the optical detector, as its name implies, reacts to the visible products of combustion, i.e. the particles of carbon and other chemicals which give smoke its characteristic appearance. An optical detector has two important components, a light source and a photo-electric cell. It is the amount of light falling on the photo-electric cell, which is the critical factor in the operation of the optical detector. Some optical detectors are designed so that, in a fire situation, MORE light is thrown onto the photo-electric cell. These are called the 'light-scatter type'. Others are designed so that LESS light is thrown onto the photo-electric cell in a fire situation. These are called 'obscuration type'.

a. The light-scatter type

(1) The theory

The light source and the photo-electric cell are mounted in a light-proof housing which is designed to allow smoke to flow into it unimpeded. In the 'non-fire' condition light from the light source does not fall on to the photo-electric cell. Fig. 11.6 shows a light-scatter type in this condition.

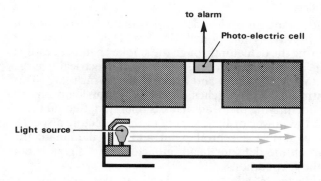

Fig. 11.6 An optical smoke detector 'light-scatter' type (non-fire condition).

When smoke particles enter the housing, however, some light is deflected upwards onto the photo-electric cell. In response to the light falling onto it the cell will either create an electrical current in the detector circuit or allow more current to flow through it (depending on the type of cell being used). The small increase in current is normally amplified by a transistorised circuit in order to energise a relay which controls the alarm. The detector is preset so that the alarm is given when the smoke density reaches a predetermined level (Fig. 11.7).

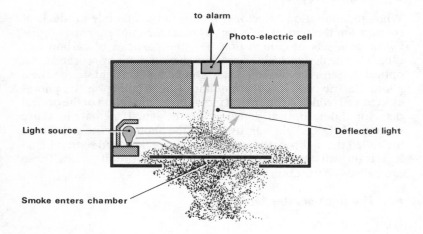

Fig. 11.7 An optical smoke detector 'light-scatter' type (fire condition).

(2) The practice

The 'light-scatter type' of optical detector is the more common of the two types previously mentioned. See Fig. 11.8 and Plate 9.

Smoke entering the detector through the smoke chamber scatters light onto the photo-electric cell. The small electrical charge produced by this is amplified and actuates an alarm relay. This raises the alarm and also switches on the indicator lamp on the detector, thus identifying the head that has operated. Should there be a failure in the power or light supply in the detector, a special relay will signal this at a central point and also illuminate the indicator lamp on the detector head; an actual 'fire' signal is not produced in these conditions.

The area protected by a detector head will vary depending on the risk involved, the floor plan and other variables, the nominal area coverage for the detector illustrated in Fig. 11.8 is 100 square metres per head. As with the ionisation detector it is possible with modifications, to mount some optical detectors in air ducts etc.

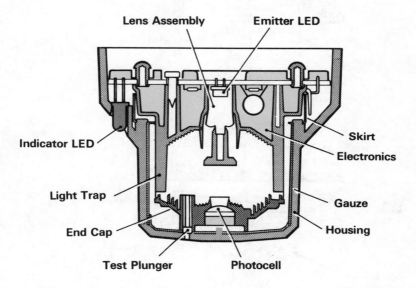

Fig. 11.8 Kidde optical smoke detector.

b.   Obscuration type

(1)   The theory

The obscuration type optical detector works on the reverse of the principle just described – the light is obscured by the smoke. The resultant reduction in the intensity of light falling on the photo-electric cell causes an alarm signal to be raised. This principle is illustrated in Fig. 11.9.

(2)   The practice

This type of optical detector can be particularly useful for the protection of large areas. It is possible with only one detector to throw the light beam up to 100 metres with a sensitivity of about 7 metres on either side. The light source and lens will be housed at one end of the protected area with the photo-electric cell at the opposite end (this is similar to the arrangement for the infra-red beam fire detection system described on page 127). The principle can also be used in individual detector heads on a similar basis to the light-scatter type.

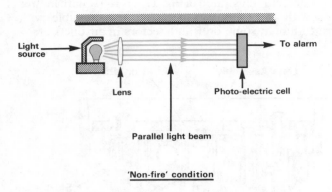

'Non-fire' condition

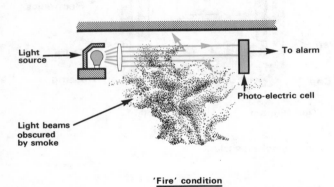

'Fire' condition

Fig. 11.9 Optical detector – 'obscuration' type.

Light emitting diodes (L.E.D's) are now widely used as the light source in optical detectors instead of tungsten filament lamps. They consume very little current and provide a more efficient and longer lasting source of light.

c.   Sampling detector

Sampling detectors comprise probe tubes located in the fire-risk zone and they are connected to a monitoring unit which contains the actual smoke detector. This monitoring unit continuously samples the atmosphere in the protected zone by drawing air in through the small holes in the probes either by fan or by using a differential in pressure between two probes. The air is then passed through the detector chamber which is set to operate when any combustion products reach a certain level.

This type of detector is mainly fitted into ducts and must be positioned correctly to operate at maximum efficiency. The airflow, at the position, should be between 1 to 10 metres/sec and away from areas of turbulence e.g. bends, fans, intersections. Care must also be taken that a common duct does not extract from too many points because the amount of any smoke may then become too diluted to operate the detector.

An example of a duct smoke detector is shown in Fig. 11.10.

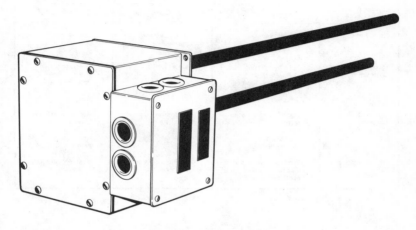

Fig. 11.10 GENT 7500 duct optical smoke detector.

d. Linear beam detector
This type are both smoke and heat detectors and are more fully discussed in Chapter 13.

e. Conclusion
The detection of fire by smoke detectors is dependent on a number of factors, e.g. smoke concentration, size, and shape of smoke particles (see Chapter 17 Section 2). The wide variety of smoke produced by different materials complicates the situation. In the early stages of most fires the smoke particles are small, but as the fire develops they tend to conglomerate to form larger particles.

The ionisation detector is generally more sensitive to the smaller, normally visible, smoke particles. This makes it particularly useful in the early stages of relatively clean burning fires (e.g. of wood and paper). It will not, however, always operate in the presence of 'cold' smoke. The optical detector is more efficient in situations where the protected risk is likely to give rise to dense smoke (i.e. larger particles) in the earlier stages of a fire as in some burning plastics.

In the main earlier detection can be obtained with a smoke sensitive system than with a heat sensitive one. Table 12 gives a summary of the advantages and disadvantages.

Table 12

Type	Operation	Advantages	Disadvantages
Beam Detector	Smoke obscures infra-red beam	Can be used for large ducts. Sensitive.	Large and expensive.
Ionization Duct Detector	Tube penetrating airflow diverts a sample to a chamber containing the detector.	Inexpensive	Selects only part of the airflow. Detector is sensitive to airflow speed.
Optical Duct Detector	Light coloured smoke scatters infra-red beams inside the chamber to a infra-red sensor.	Inexpensive Sensitive	Measures only part of the airflow. Reacts best to light coloured smoke.
Air Sampling System	Tubes sample air and pass to a chamber, containing a detector.	Efficient for large duct networks.	Measures only part of the airflow.

Chapter 12
Radiation detectors

As well as producing hot 'gases' fire releases radiant energy (Fig. 12.1) in the form of:

(i)   Infra-red radiation

(ii)   Visible light

(iii)   Ultra-violet radiation.

These forms of energy travel in waves radiating from their point of origin and radiation detectors are designed to respond to this radiation.

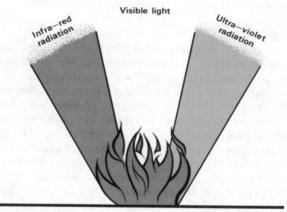

Fig. 12.1 Forms of radiant energy produced by a fire.

Obviously the use of the visible light band to activate a detector would present many problems because the detector would not be able to differentiate between the various legitimate sources of visible light and those created by a fire. In practice therefore these detectors are designed to respond specifically to either:

(1)   Infra-red radiation

or

(2)   ultra violet radiation

using a device which is sensitive to one of these sources.

109

1 Infra-red detector

The basic components of the infra-red detector are shown in Fig. 12.2.

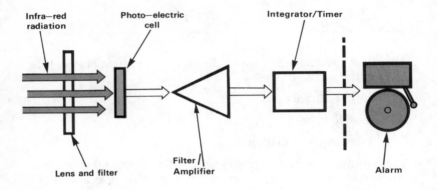

Fig. 12.2 Schematic diagram of components of an infra-red detector.

It is obviously necessary to protect the photo-electric cell and electrical components from dirt and moisture but the protective covering must allow the infra-red radiation to pass through it. Not all material is transparent to infra-red but quartz is and is commonly used as the protective shield in these detectors. The lens and filter will allow only infra-red radiation to fall on to the photo-electric cell. On detecting the radiation, the cell will transmit a signal to the filter/amplifier. Flame, however, may not be the only producer of infra-red radiation in the protected area; there may be a limited number of other producers e.g. sunlight or heaters, but flame has a distinctive flicker, normally in the frequency range of 4Hz–15Hz. The function of the filter/amplifier, therefore, is not only to amplify but also to filter out signals not in this range. If the signal is in this range (4Hz–15Hz) it is then fed to the integrator/timer which will activate the alarm circuit only if the signal persists for a pre-set period (normally 2–15 secs). While this small delay may slightly off-set the quick response time of the detector, it is necessary if false alarms are to be kept to a minimum. Once any signal is rejected the detector goes back on standby.

a. Fixed types

Fig. 12.3 shows how these components can be fitted into an actual detector.

This detector has a neon flasher to indicate which head has been activated.

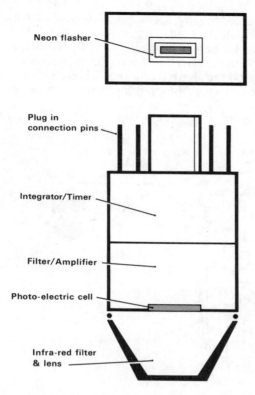

Neon flasher

Plug in
connection pins

Integrator/Timer

Filter/Amplifier

Photo-electric cell

Infra-red filter
& lens

Fig. 12.3 Schematic diagram of an infra-red radiation detector.

As an infra-red detector must 'see' a flame before it will raise an alarm, the one illustrated in Fig. 12.3 is useful where the risk is divided into compartments or is a congested area in which visibility might be impaired. Individual detector heads can protect each compartment or be placed in strategic positions in the congested area.

b. Scanning type

For larger areas, free of congestion and with a more open plan, a scanning infra-red detector is available. One of these is illustrated in Plate 10 and Fig. 12.4.

The detector continually scans the protected area (approximately every 20 seconds). This enables the detector to monitor 360 degrees in the horizontal plane and a wide angle on the vertical plane. Immediately the photo-electric cell is struck by deflected infra-red radiation and the characteristic 'flicker' is identified by the filter/amplifier, the integrator stops the motor in order that the deflector

111

can 'view' the flame source directly and allow radiation to fall continuously on the photo-electric cell.

The timer can then check whether the flame flicker persists for the 12–15 seconds as explained earlier. Where the infra-red source is present beyond this period the alarm is raised; if it is not present the integrator restarts the deflector motor putting the detector back on standby.

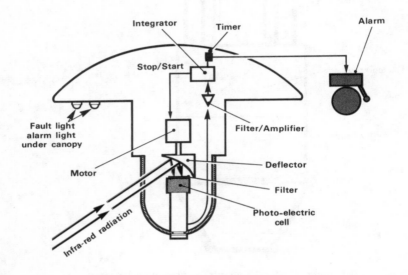

Fig. 12.4 Diagram of a scanning infra-red radiation detector.

The infra-red scan detector has an amber fault light which will light up a few seconds after a fault is detected; the red alarm light illuminates once the integrator activates the alarm.

The domed cover is thermally insulated and the cell and deflector are shielded by a quartz globe.

Theoretically there is no limit to the range of the infra-red scan detector but, for quick detection in the early stages of a fire, the radius of detection should be limited to about 90 metres.

A much greater area of coverage can be obtained from the scanning type than from the static type but which type is used in any particular situation will depend on the interior plan and use of the protected area. Infra-red detectors can provide rapid detection in risk areas where flame is likely to develop at an early stage of combustion. This is because of the almost instantaneous transmission of radiation.

Unlike smoke or heat detectors which can only be used indoors, the infra-red detector can be equally efficient inside or out. This is because it simply needs to 'see' the flame, whereas smoke or heat detectors have to rely on ceiling or walls to direct combustion products to the sensing device. This ability makes the infra-red detector (especially the scanning type) useful for protection of open storage areas, aircraft maintenance areas (both inside and out) etc. However, some problems occasionally arise due to sunlight, rippling pools of water, welding etc. but modern detectors incorporate integrated circuits which can filter out these potential false alarms.

2 Ultra-violet detector

a. The theory

Like the infra-red detector, this UV detector also needs to be able to 'see' the flame before it will operate, but since legitimate sources of UV radiation are very limited, flicker discrimination is not needed.

Basically the UV detector consists of an amplifier and a photo-electric cell of gas-filled tube sensitive to UV radiation (Fig. 12.5).

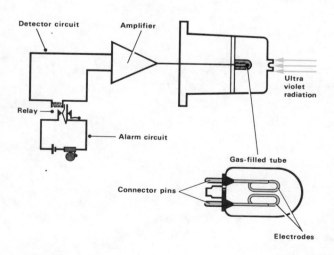

Fig. 12.5 Diagram of an ultra-violet detector.

b. The practice

When UV radiation strikes the gas-filled tube it ionises the gas in the tube. A small current is set up between the two electrodes and the tube becomes a conductor of electricity. When the current flow is greater than the set point of the amplifier the alarm relay closes immediately and causes the alarm to sound. The circuit can also have an integrator incorporated in it which will effectively delay the alarm for 10–15 seconds. This can reduce false alarms from legitimate external sources of radiation e.g. lightning.

The detector is not affected by sunlight or artificial light but is sensitive to electrical arcs and would not therefore be recommended for areas in which welding was being done.

In practice the UV detector is most commonly used for specialised applications such as monitoring of aircraft engine nacelles, but it can be used to protect fuel storage tanks, oil drilling rigs, warehouses, paint spray booths etc.

c. Conclusion

UV radiation detectors have a quick response capability but do not need a clear 'view' of the protected area. Here, as with infra-red, they are superior to heat and smoke detectors. One factor to be borne in mind is that they are inferior to infra-red detectors in penetrating smoke.

Chapter 13
Heat detectors

Heat detectors are designed to detect fire in its more advanced stages when the temperature in the protected area starts to rise. Given that the effects of heat are easy to observe it is not surprising that heat detectors were the earliest form of detector to be developed.

The effects of heat which provide the basic operating principles for heat detectors are:

(1) Melting (or fusion) in metals or plastics

(2) Expansion in solids, gases and liquids

(3) The electrical effect.

These allow a wide choice in methods of heat detection. This chapter explains, in turn, each one of the above effects and detectors which use them. In discussing heat detectors reference will be made to *'fixed temperature'* detectors and *'rate-of-rise'* detectors. A 'fixed temperature' detector is one that responds only when a predetermined temperature is reached.

A 'rate-of-rise' detector is one that responds when the temperature rise is abnormally rapid.

In practice 'rate-of-rise' detectors generally incorporate a fixed temperature device in accordance with BS 3316 for heat detectors. This is particularly useful where a very slow growing fire would not generate heat sufficiently rapidly to operate the 'rate-of-rise' element.

1 Heat detectors using fusible alloys

a. The theory
This type of detector is based on the fact that certain metal alloys and plastics melt at relatively low temperatures, the general range available being between 55°C to 180°C. As the metal/plastic used determines the temperature at which the alarm will sound it will be chosen for the type of risk to be protected and the normal ambient temperature in that protected area.

115

Although firefighters will come across obsolescent types using fusible metal/plastic most, if not all, have been superseded by more modern devices and will not be described here. It should be borne in mind that fusible alloy sprinkler heads and the fusible links found, for instance, across the front of oil-fired boilers (see the Manual Part 6c, Section 5) are all heat detectors of this particular type.

2 Heat detectors using the principle of expansion

a. Expansion of a single metal strip

A piece of metal will expand when heated; this expansion is most noticeable in a length of metal with its ends unrestrained.

If both ends of the metal are secured to a solid base and the metal is then subjected to heat the effect of the expansion is to cause the metal strip to bow (Fig. 13.1). If contacts are added, as shown in the diagram, the principle can be used in a detector to complete an electrical circuit when a predetermined temperature is reached.

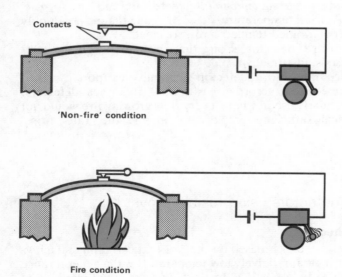

Fig. 13.1 Illustration of the expansion of a metal strip with secured ends.

b. Expansion of a bi-metallic strip

The bi-metallic strip is a development of the basic principle of metal expansion due to heat and makes use of the fact that, when heated, some metals expand at a greater rate than others (Fig. 13.2), (see the Manual, Book 1, Chapter 3).

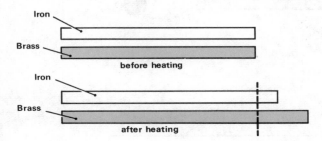

Fig. 13.2 Illustration of differing rates of metal expansion.

If these two metals are bonded together to form a bi-metallic strip and then subjected to heat the strip will bend (Fig. 13.3) to accommodate the differing rates of expansion. Fig. 13.4 shows a simple example of the use of a bi-metallic strip as a heat detector.

The advantage of a bi-metallic strip over a single metal strip is the greater movement resulting from a given rise in temperature.

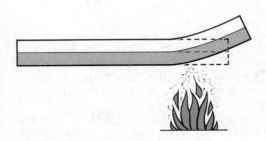

Fig. 13.3 The effect of heat on a bimetallic strip.

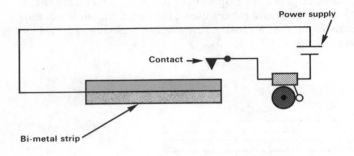

'Non-fire' condition

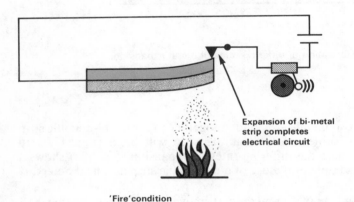

'Fire' condition

Fig. 13.4 An example of a bimetallic strip used as a heat detector.

c. Gent 1151

The Gent 1151 heat detector (Fig. 13.5) uses a bi-metallic strip as a heat sensing element. The strip is attached to a hinged platform assembly held in place by a mechanical latch. This assembly also houses a mercury switch.

At a predetermined temperature (normally 58°C), the bi-metallic strip bows and causes a pillar to move upwards releasing the mechanical latch. The platform assembly hinges down and, in an open-circuit detector, the mercury in the tilted tube covers the electrical contacts and completes the circuit thereby causing the alarm to sound.

In an alternative closed-circuit detector, the tilting of the mercury switch breaks an electrical circuit to achieve the same result. Chapter 15 explains the theory of open and closed circuits in greater detail.

The tilting of the lower portion of the detector allows for quick identification of the head that has operated.

Each detector can protect an area of 36 square metres.

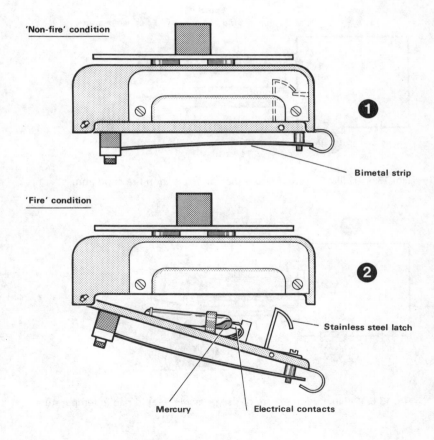

Fig. 13.5 GENT 1151 heat detector. (1) Non-fire condition. (2) Fire condition.

d. Expansion of bi-metallic strips in a 'rate-of-rise' detector

(1) The theory

Bi-metallic strips are also used as the heat sensitive elements in some 'rate-of-rise' detectors. The principle of operation is explained below (and see (f)(2)).

Two similar composition bi-metallic strips are used but one is suitably shielded and protected to reduce its rate of expansion (Fig. 13.6(1)). If there is a rapid rise in temperature (Fig. 13.6 (2)) strip (1), which is not shielded, will expand more rapidly than strip (2) and, as a result, will quickly cause the two electrical contacts to come together.

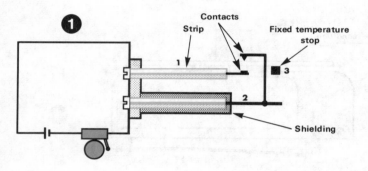

Fig. 13.6. (1) Illustration of rate-of-rise principle (non-fire condition).

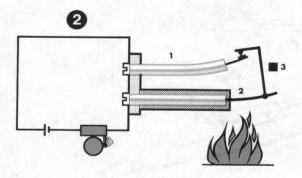

Fig. 13.6. (2) Illustration of rate-of-rise principle – rapid rise in temperature.

Where there is a slow rise in temperature, which may be for reasons unconnected with the fire, (Fig. 13.6 (3)) the slow rate of expansion in both strips keeps them, roughly, the same distance apart and the contacts do not touch. It is undesirable however for this situation to continue too long because a slow burning fire might be the cause of the temperature rise. For this reason (as mentioned at the beginning of this Chapter) a fixed temperature device (3) is usually fitted in 'rate-of-rise' detectors. This will stop the movement of strip (2) when a predetermined temperature is reached and thus allow strip (1) to close the contacts and raise the alarm.

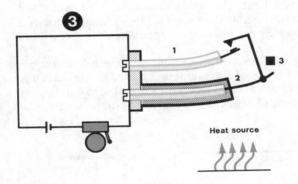

Fig. 13.6. (3) Illustration of rate-of-rise princple – slow rise in temperature.

e. Advantages and disadvantages

The main advantage of detectors operating on the expansion-of-metal principle is that they suffer no damage from operation and are generally self-resetting. They are therefore back on standby automatically immediately any fire has been dealt with. This does not, of course, apply to detectors operating on the Gent 1151 principle – in these cases the metal strip housing will have to be pushed into place.

Where there is likely to be a large but gradual variation in ambient temperature during normal processes, the 'rate-of-rise' detector has the advantage of giving a quick response to any sudden abnormal temperature rise whilst minimising the number of false alarms.

However, where a rapid rise in temperature is a normal result of work processes, the fixed temperature detector is to be preferred. In this type of situation it is less prone to false alarms than the 'rate-of-rise' type.

A fixed temperature detector will take longer to respond in a cold area than in a warm one. This is because of the longer time needed for the ambient temperature to reach the operating temperature of the detector. A 'rate-of-rise' type on the other hand will take the same time to respond in both situations – it reacts to the relative rise in temperature.

f.   Expansion of gases

(1)   The theory

Where gas is used as the expanding element in a heat detector, air is the gas most commonly used; such detectors are sometimes referred to as pneumatic detectors.

The basic operating principle of this type of detector is illustrated in Fig. 13.7.

When subjected to heat, the air in the chamber expands and applies pressure to the flexible diaphragm. This gradually pushes it up until it meets the electrical contact, completes the circuit and raises the alarm.

By producing a small compensating vent into the side of the air chamber (Fig. 13.7) a rate-of-rise element is added to the detector. The compensating vent will allow a certain amount of expanding air to escape; it will be carefully calibrated so as to compensate in the ambient temperature.

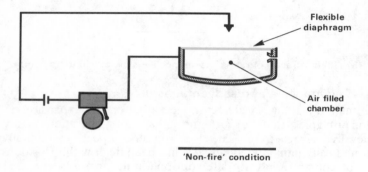

'Non-fire' condition

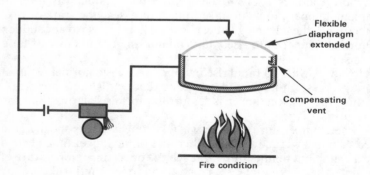

Fire condition

Fig. 13.7 Illustration of the principle of a pneumatic detector.

(2)   Chubb type H – rate-of-rise detector

This point detector (Fig. 13.8 and Plate 12) operates on the principle of expansion of air for the rate-of-rise element, and a bi-metallic disc for the fixed temperature element.

The detector head comprises a circular white plastic moulding to which is attached a metal cap forming a sealed chamber. The upper surface of the air chamber includes a diaphragm and a leak which communicates with the upper part of the detector. The rapid rise of ambient temperature due to a fire causes an equally rapid expansion of air inside the chamber. This deflects the centre of the diaphragm (1) which rises to make an electrical contact (2). This triggers the circuit to 'fire' condition, sounds the alarm and illuminates the 'fire' indicator (3) in the detector and, if necessary, the remote indicator on the panel.

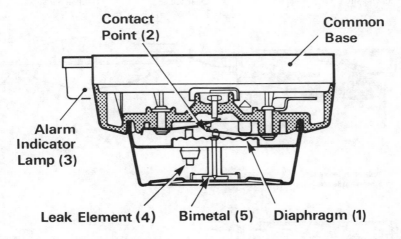

Contact Point (2)   **Common Base**

Alarm Indicator Lamp (3)

Leak Element (4)   **Bimetal (5)**   **Diaphragm (1)**

Fig. 13.8 Chubb rate-of-rise detector.

If the ambient temperature increases slowly air is leaked through the leak element (4) to compensate for the local fluctuation but, should the rise persist, a bimetallic disc (5) deflects the centre of the diaphragm at the predetermined temperature to indicate the 'fire' condition. Preset temperatures are 60°C and 90°C depending on the type of detector required.

(3)   The 'Kidde' pneumatic 'rate-of-rise' heat detecting system

This system uses a hollow copper chamber as the detector head (Plate 13). It is filled with air at normal atmospheric pressure. These heads are sometimes referred to as Heat Actuated Devices (or H.A.D's). Normally fixed to the ceiling each head is connected by small bore copper tubing to a control head which houses a flexible diaphragm, a release lever and a compensating vent (Fig. 13.9). When a detector head is subjected to heat the increasing air pressure due to expansion is transmitted through the copper tubing to the control head.

If the expansion is due to normal fluctuations in the ambient temperature, the pressure is released through the compensating vent and the diaphragm and release lever remain unaffected.

Where the rate of increase in pressure is above that allowed for by the compensating vent the diaphragm will be depressed and in turn will push down the release lever (Fig. 13.9). This completes an electrical circuit and activates the alarm.

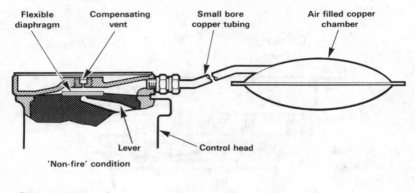

'Non-fire' condition

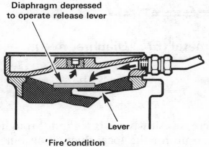

'Fire' condition

Fig. 13.9 Diagrammatic illustration of a Kidde pneumatic heat detecting system.

These detector heads have, of course, no moving parts to go wrong.

Although this is primarily a 'rate-of-rise' system it is possible to create a 'fixed temperature' version. To achieve this the detector is fitted with a slug of metal which seals the head from the diaphragm until the slug of metal melts at a predetermined temperature (a range from 57°C upwards is available). The metal slug will of course need replacing each time the detector head operates.

This arrangement is particularly useful where the 'devices' connected to one control head cover a variety of risks – each 'device' can be left as 'rate-of-rise' or made 'fixed temperature' as necessary.

Usually six 'rate-of-rise' heat actuated devices are fitted to one control head. Where, however, 'rate-of-rise' and 'fixed temperature' types are being used in the same system, the combined number can be more.

The area protected by one heat actuated device will be affected by the plan and the use being made of the area. It can vary from 27–72 square metres.

j   Expansion of liquids

Sprinkler systems

The liquid filled quartzoid bulbs used in sprinkler systems are probably the most common form of heat detector operating on the the expansion of liquid principle (see Chapter 5).

Many of the detection systems discussed in this Part are, in practice, linked with sprinkler or other extinguishing systems. Once activated the detector not only raises the alarm but also causes the sprinkler system to release extinguishing agent into the affected area. In many cases this arrangement can reduce sprinkler response time (see Chapter 3 Section 4)

3   Linear heat detectors (LHD)

a.   General

There is a problem when protecting cable tunnels, conveyors and similar areas with lengthy runs. Point detectors may have to be unacceptably close, or dense, to be effective. Flame detectors are a method but, with cables, flame is not necessarily the first mainifestation of fire, and beam detectors have to depend on the configuration of the tunnel etc.

A line of sensing material which can follow the contours of the risk are obviously a method and this is generally known as linear detection.

There are, at the moment, three types:–

(i)   relying on the effect of heat on electrical resistivity;

(ii)   relying on the effect of heat on the insulation between two conductors; and

(iii)   relying on the melting of a thermo-plastic tube containing compressed air or an inert gas.

All three are able to detect overheat conditions possibly even before a fire occurs and can, for instance in a cable tunnel, follow the risk closely wherever it runs (see Fig. 13.10).

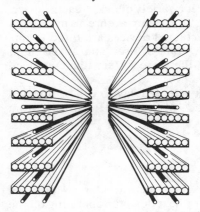

Fig. 13.10 Linear heat detecting cables protecting a cable tunnel.

b. Operating methods

(1) Resistivity type

In this type the conductors are separated by a sensitive di-electrical material which, when subjected to heat, decreases in resistance and allows a measurable leakage current to develop (Fig. 13.11).

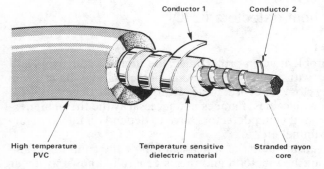

Conductor 1   Conductor 2

High temperature
PVC

Temperature sensitive
dielectric material

Stranded rayon
core

Fig. 13.11 Example of detector cable.

This type is limited in the length of risk zone that it can cover. This is, basically, because resistivity is not only related to temperature but also to length. An advantage, however, is that, following an overheat condition, the LHD will reset, providing that it has not been damaged or destroyed by the fire. This type can also be programmed to take account of different ambient temperatures prevailing in any zone it passes through.

(2) Insulation type

This type relies on the melting, at a pre-determined temperature, of the insulation separating two conductors, A fire alarm is, therefore, indicated by a short circuit, whilst an open circuit gives a fault indication.

There is no limitation on the length of this type but that section of the cable which has detected the fire will have to be replaced.

(3) Compressed gas type

Some areas to be protected are very hostile to types (1) and (2). This third type utilises a thermo-plastic small-bore tube fed by a source of compressed air (or inert gas) at, perhaps, about 5 bar pressure. This pressure is used to hold back a mechanism which, when the pressure is released, trips and transmits the alarm. The tube is designed to melt at a certain temperature within a 5 per cent tolerance.

It is relatively inexpensive to install and replace when it is damaged or has detected a fire. It is basically mechanical and any fall in pressure, e.g. due to leaks or damage, will raise the alarm.

4 Beam detectors

All detectors discussed in this chapter so far have been 'point' detectors but there are also rules governing the recommended positioning of beam detectors.

A beam detector is a combined head and smoke detector consisting of two units; a transmitter producing a pulsed beam of infra-red light generated by a gallium arsenide LED (light emitting diode) and a monitor receiver tuned to accept that frequency

The two units are mounted at opposite ends of the space to be protected, the distance between the units must not be more than 100 metres for a single beam (BS 5839). The minimum height, in an area where people are moving about is 2.7 metres, the maximum height is 25 metres, but this can be increased to 40 metres provided that, generally, combustibles are not stored more than 5 metres high in that building or compartment (BS 5839). Depending on the circumstances and risk, beams should be placed to achieve the greatest efficiency but the horizontal distance between them (measured at right angles to the beam) should not be more than 14 metres. Normally critical alignment between the two units is not essential because the beam is relatively wide.

The principles of operation are as follows. The infra-red beam produced by the transmitter is analysed by the receiver photo sensor for loss of strength caused by smoke obscuration (see Fig. 13.12(b)) and for fluctuations caused by thermal turbulance (see Fig.

13.12(a)). When either of the phenomena exceeds a pre-set level the 'smoke' or 'heat' LED is illuminated and a fire signal is transmitted. (The receiver also contains LED's indicating 'fault' or 'normal' conditions).

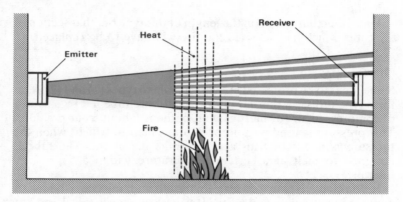

Fig. 13.12(A) Effect of flame on an infra-red beam detector.

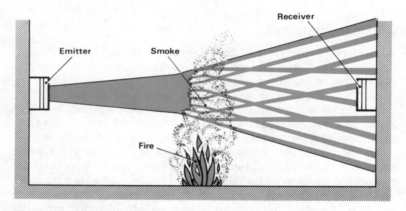

Fig. 13.12(B) Effect of smoke on infra-red beam detector.

Another type of beam detector works on the same principal but uses retro-reflectors. After the beam has crossed the protected area, it is reversed by the retro-reflectors, focused by the large lens and monitored by the receiver within the same housing as the emitter.

Both these types of detectors can distinguish low changes in ambient temperature or build-up of dust on either of the screens by continually comparing the received beam intensity with previous levels.

This type of detector is effective for use in large premises, particularly long, high buildings for example; aircraft hangars, museums, open-plan offices, areas with radioactive risks etc.

5   General comment on heat detectors

Heat detectors, and the 'fixed temperature' type in particular, are dependent for their operation on heat being transferred from the surrounding air to the detector itself. As the air will heat more quickly than the detector, the operating element in the detector will usually be at slightly lower temperature than the surrounding air. This difference in temperature is referred to as thermal lag and could in some circumstances delay a detector's response. Its extent will depend on a number of factors e.g. the surface area of the detector, the amount and speed of air passing the device.

This is an important point to be borne in mind when deciding on the suitability and desirable operating temperature of 'fixed temperature' detectors. These are not generally suitable for use in very cold areas or locations which are subjected to strong currents of fresh air.

Chapter 14
Automatic fire detectors
Radio-based systems

1 General

In the last 10–15 years, systems have been developed using radio transmitters connected to detectors. These are designed to signal faults or fires to a central receiver which would carry out all the conventional functions e.g. sound an alarm, indicate the detector's position, call the brigade.

The detectors are all of a conventional type and they, together with the transmitters, form entirely separate units energised mainly by batteries (see 4 below). The receiver/control is conventionally powered as required by BS5839.

Usually the transmitters all operate on the same frequency in any one system, but each transmitter has its own modulation which is decoded by the receiver. Further pulse length coding differentiates between fire and fault signals, and the detectors can also be designed to 'report in' periodically to ensure that the transmission path between transmitter and receiver is still effective (see 3(b)(iv)).

2 Safeguards

Various safeguards are built in to prevent interference by outside radio signals and to prevent the system interfering with other electronic equipment e.g. computers. The system can also be zoned i.e. a number of detectors can be designed to give a common signal.

Radio repeater stations can be installed where local screening is a problem.

3 Advantages and disadvantages

a. The advantages of a radio system are:-

(i) It is quick to install with no wiring and, therefore, no requirement to redecorate which, in turn, means little disturbance.

(ii) The risk of wiring damage which could isolate several detectors is avoided.

(iii)   The location of the detectors is flexible e.g. they can be installed in buildings under construction or areas where partitions are frequently moved.

(iv)   Radio links will function even in a fire situation, so there is no need for special fire-protected cabling.

(v)   Extra zones can easily be connected to the main receiver, or remote indicator panels set up.

b.   Disadvantages

(i)   The initial capital cost of the equipment is relatively high.

(ii)   Temporary screening may occur, although frequent 'report-ins' will indicate this fairly quickly.

(iii)   The system has to be designed very carefully to avoid clashes of frequencies and interference either into or from the system (see 2 above).

(iv)   There may be a significant delay between occurrence of a fault and its indication on the control equipment. This arises because limitations of allowed frequency spectrum can lead to interference between simultaneous signals at very frequent intervals. The code suggests that radio links be monitored so that, if signals are not received from any remote component, the failure will be indicated at the central control and indicating equipment within 4–5 hours of the fault occurring.

4   Power supplies

BS5389 recommends the types of power supplies for detectors and manual call points forming part of a radio interconnected system:-

(i)   The normal mains supply plus a reserve battery (primary or continuously charged secondary)

(ii)   a primary battery plus a reserve second primary battery. The primary battery used for the normal supply should have an operational life of, at least, one year.

(iii)   Power supplies having one, or more, primary batteries are required to give at least 30 days warning of impending failure of any primary battery.

Chapter 15
Automatic fire detection –
detector circuits

The function of the detector circuit in an automatic detection system is to transmit the signal given by the activated detector head (or manual call point) to a centrally situated control and indicating equipment from which the alarm is raised. In practice these processes occur simultaneously.

Basically there are two types of detector circuit:

(i)   'Open' circuit

(ii)   'Closed' circuit

their condition being reversed in each case to raise the alarm.

1   'Open' circuit – the theory

In an 'open' circuit system detectors or call points are wired in parallel and can be regarded as switches in the 'off' position i.e. there is no current flow when in standby. The operation of a detector effectively closes the contacts and activates the alarm system.

As there is no current flow when on standby it is not self monitoring; as a result, however, it does not consume as much electricity as a 'closed' circuit and is therefore cheaper to run. A short circuit in the detector wiring will raise an alarm, as it effectively closes the circuit. A broken circuit, on the other hand, will not and if unidentified could render some detector heads inoperative.

It is important to remember that in all except the simplest systems the detector and alarm circuits are separate – meeting only in the alarm control unit (for simplicity this has been omitted from Figs. 15.1 and 15.2).

2   'Closed' circuit – the theory

'Closed' circuit detectors (or call points) can be regarded as a series of switches whose contacts are normally closed when the system is on standby thus allowing current to flow in the detector circuit. This current energises the relay which holds contact (1) (Fig. 15.2) against contact (3) and keeps the alarm circuit inoperative. Once a detector (or call point) operates the detector circuit is broken interrupting current flow to the relay.

The relay is therefore de-energised releasing contact (1) which springs back to contact (2), completing the alarm circuit and sounding the bells.

The main advantage of this type of circuit is that the continuous current on standby makes it partly self monitoring. Any break in the detector circuit will cause the alarm to ring; which, although it may be false, does at least draw attention to the fault. The fact that the circuit is drawing current from the supply on standby can be regarded as a disadvantage – the size and cost of the battery and charger will be increased. Also in a basic 'closed' circuit system a short circuit could remain unnoticed as it simply completes a separate path for current flow. In doing this it could by-pass some detectors and call points, rendering them inoperative.

3 Detector and alarm circuits – the practice

It is essential that detector and alarm circuits are reliable. The diagrams in Figs. 15.1 and 15.2 are basic illustrations of 'open' and 'closed' circuits. In practice the circuitry, although based on these principles, is more sophisticated than this. Ring circuits and other refinements can be used to achieve, as far as possible, a fail-safe situation and to overcome the disadvantage mentioned earlier. Sophisticated electronic circuitry is incorporated to reduce false alarms by providing for separate signalling of fault conditions (e.g. a broken circuit or a short circuit).

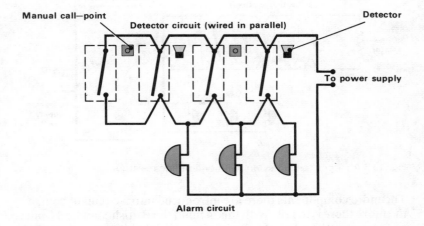

Fig. 15.1 Diagram of an 'open' circuit system.

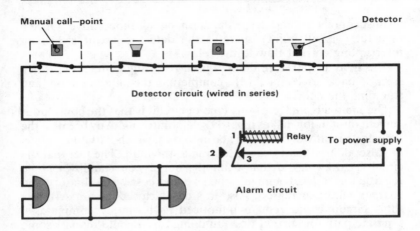

Fig. 15.2 Diagram of a 'closed' circuit system.

Closed circuits have the advantage mentioned earlier that they are continuously under test i.e. current flows in the circuit on standby. If desired, however, the continuity of an 'open' circuit can be tested incorporating an end-of-line resistor in the circuit (Fig. 15.3).

This allows a continuous but reduced current flow through the detector circuit. The continuity of the flow will be monitored at the control unit. The resistor incorporated in the circuit reduces the current sufficiently to prevent it activating the alarms.

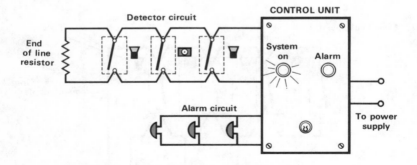

Fig. 15.3 An 'open' circuit sytem with end-of-line resistors.

The more components there are introduced into a circuit of course, the more there is to fail. With this in mind the British Standard Code of Practice 1019 states 'In the interests of reliability it is desirable that the number of circuit elements in the system . . . should be kept to a minimum . . . Every additional component will inevitably add some risk. Nevertheless with care taken to minimise these a fully discriminating system can be well justified'. The BS/LPC Rules require some element of discrimination (e.g. fault signalling or end-of-line testing) in approved systems.

Some detectors and manual call points can be used in either 'open' or 'closed' circuits.

4   Wiring and power supplies

a.   Wiring

It is essential for reliability that the wiring in automatic fire alarm systems should be of high standard and suitably protected against the possibility of accidental damage. The thermostatic cable described on page 127 can be used for wiring open detector circuits – it is mainly used with heat detectors.

b.   Power supplies

Obviously an adequate and reliable power supply must be available to automatic detection and alarm systems.

This can be a mains supply or a battery supply. In either case BS/LPC Rules require that a standby supply must be automatically available in the event of a failure in the primary supply. The standby supply will normally be a battery maintained in a fully-charged state. This supply can be automatically brought into operation by incorporating a changeover relay in the circuit.

Most modern systems will incorporate a system of automatically giving warning of a change over to a secondary supply. Also there will be a requirement varying in the length of time according to the risk that the secondary supply will maintain the whole system until the defect is remedied (see Chapter 14 Section 4).

Chapter 16
Control and indicating equipment

1 General

The introduction of BS 3316 Part 4 'Control and indicating equipment' resulted in a radical revision of system requirements. It brought in the concept of system fault monitoring and indication and also emphasised enhanced system reliability requiring the use of dual power supplies. These requirements have now been absorbed into BS 5839 Part 1 1988.

It meant that control system manufacturers had to look to electronic components and advance their systems in line with current technology.

2 Zones

Nowadays a fire alarm system of any size will be based on zones within the protected premises. This enables the indicator boards to show, more precisely, the whereabouts of the origin of the signal. Depending on the sophistication of the system this will be a visual and audible indication plus, possibly, a logging printout of the exact location of the actuated device within the zone. Other simpler systems will just indicate the zone as an illuminated sign of a certain colour denoting the states of the signal plus an audible signal.

BS 5839 Part 1 makes certain recommendations for the size and number of zones:-

(i) The floor area of any single zone should not exceed $200m^2$.

(ii) The 'search distance' i.e. the distance that has to be travelled by a searcher inside a zone in order to, visually, determine the position of the fire, should not exceed $30m^2$.

(iii) If the total floor area of a building exceeds $300m^2$ then a zone should cover only one storey. However, where detectors are fitted in stairwells, lightwells, lift-shafts and other 'fluelike' structures extending beyond one floor but within one fire compartment, the volume of the shaft should be considered as a 'separate zone'.

(iv) If the total floor area of the building is $300m^2$ or less then the building may be considered a single zone even though there may be more than one storey.

(v)   Where a zone extends beyond a single compartment the zone boundaries should be boundaries of fire compartments. It is not permissible to have a zone extending into parts of 2 compartments or a compartment which extends into parts of 2 zones.

(vi)   In premises providing sleeping accommodation the above-mentioned factors should be considered in relation to the fire routine adopted by the premises. It is of paramount importance in a life risk that the precise location of the origin of an alarm is quickly determined.

3   Power supplies

As stated, BS 5839 Part 1 requires that fire alarm systems have to have power available from two entirely separate sources. Failure of one source must leave the other capable of operating under all likely alarm conditions and for long enough to allow the necessary action to be taken to rectify the original fault.

Both supplies must be continuously monitored to ensure that an early warning of failure of either supply is given. Batteries especially must be maintained so that their capacity does not drop below the level where they would be unable to maintain the system in operation for an acceptable period after failure of the mains supply.

4   Control and indicating equipment

The control unit is the nerve centre of any system and is usually placed in a prominent position in a building to ensure that its signals will be easily seen and heard by the building's occupants, fire brigade etc.

It could be designed to perform all or any of the functions listed below:-

(i)   Receipt of signals from 'trigger devices' e.g. smoke, heat and flame detectors together with manual call points.

(ii)   Operate alarm sounders either throughout the building or in any particular sequence related to an evacuation plan for the building.

(iii)   Transmit the signal to a remote manned centre (RMC) for onward transmission to the fire brigade (if a fire signal) or other interested parties e.g. the keyholder, maintenance engineer.

(iv) Indicate from which zone the signal is coming, not only at the main indicator panel but, if necessary, at repeater indicators throughout the premises e.g. the gatehouse.

(v) Operate other signals e.g. de-activation of door-holding devices, (in hospitals, residential homes), opening smoke ventilators.

(vi) Operate fixed firefighting equipment.

This list is not comprehensive as designers are constantly adding to these functions.

Fig. 16.1 gives a schematic diagram of a possible 2-zone system and Fig. 16.2 a simple layout of a 2-zone system with some of Fig. 1's components.

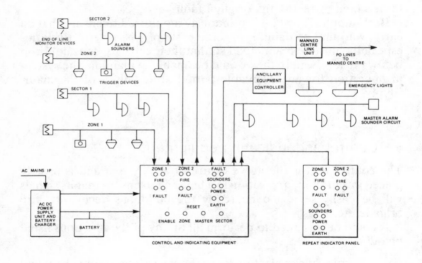

Fig. 16.1 A schematic diagram of a possible 2-zone system.

138

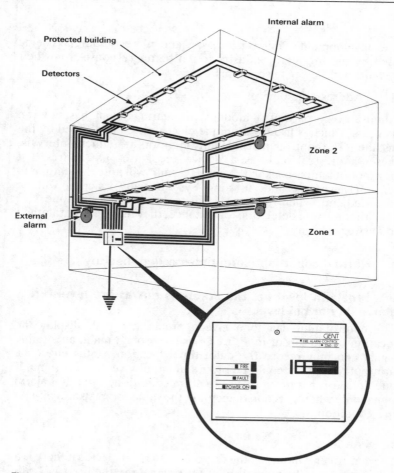

Fig. 16.2 Diagram of an automatic fire detection system showing zones and enlarge insert of control/indicator panel.

5   Faults

Fault indicating is normally done by wiring both trigger devices and alarm sounders without spur-wiring and terminating the wiring far-ends with an end-line device. This is often a resistor which is sensed by a control unit. Any break in the wire causes loss of continuity between the device and the control unit triggering a visual and audible indication of fault.

Where there is a possibility of concurrent fire and fault signals the control unit incorporates special logic circuits which differentiate between the signals and give preference to fire signals. Other fault monitoring circuits include those for power supplies.

6 Developments

The development of micro-processors and microcomputers is being used by the fire alarm industry to get better response from their systems with fewer false alarms.

(i)   Addressable devices

Almost every part of a modern fire-alarm system has now an 'address' which is usually a unique electronic code decided by the installer. The control unit constantly monitors at frequent intervals, these 'addresses' and, as a device recognises its 'address', it transmits its status back to the unit. The unit will note the status and react if necessary and, in some systems, any reaction will be recorded and, when requested, will respond with a printout.

With sensors in detectors, for instance, they may be programmed to answer.

a.   Normal condition (sometimes called 'healthy')

b.   Prealarm level i.e. the status is not at fire level but is above its normal level.

The control unit can then give a prealarm signal, display the location of the sensor in an LCD visual display, make an audible signal and may record the date, time, location, status etc. on a printout. A system could be programmed to give an alert signal if one detector in a room moves to a fire condition, and a full alarm signal only when a second detector in the same room also signifies a fire condition.

c.   Fire level

The control unit monitors the response and it will decide if there is a fire. Consequently it will display a fire signal i.e. the fire LED will illuminate, the location and the time will be displayed on an LCD panel, the audible alarm will sound, alarm sounders will trigger and the signal will be transmitted to an RMC etc.

d.   Silence alarms and reset

BS 5839 requires that a system should have a silencing device which can silence general alarm sounders or, in a two-stage system, alert signals.

The operation of the device should:-

(i)   Require a manual operation

(ii)   Sound an audible alarm at the control unit

(iii)   Not cancel any visual signal of the alarm at the control unit

(iv)   Not prevent the proper receipt of alarms from any zone not already providing an alarm.

(v)   Not prevent the correct operation of any control for starting or restarting the alarm sounder.

(vi)   Not prevent the transmission of an alarm to an RMC.

The system should not be able to reset until all devices are reinstated to 'NORMAL' condition.

e.   Fault level

This is a fault on any part of the system e.g. circuitry data output, below a certain level. The fault indicator LED will illuminate, an audible alarm signal operates and, possibly, an LCD display and printout also occur. In order not to deactivate a number of sensors or a complete zone, some systems can isolate the fault device but still leave the remainder fully alert. In this case a fault is indicated and a 'device isolated' light will illuminate plus the audible alarm.

7   Monitoring the system

Other facilities which could be included in a system are:-

(a)   the unit can be programmed to note the ambient conditions in certain areas and adjust its response to the signals accordingly.

(b)   the unit can note, over a period of time, a deterioration in a sensor e.g. from an excessive accumulation of dust, excessive insect inhalation. Taking this into account it can adjust the sensors response up to a predetermined limit and, beyond that, will register a fault.

(c)   If a sensor is removed for any reason this can be noted and it will register a fault if the wrong type of sensor is re-installed or the new sensor is not coded with the correct 'address'.

8   Maintenance

If continuous logging is included in the system an engineer on regular inspection can spot trends in deterioration or areas of intermittent faults. He can carry out tests on individual devices from the control unit using a coded keypad, identify faults, or even impending faults, and take the necessary action.

9   Visual displays

The use of LED's and LCD's are examples of the types of display being used together with alphanumeric characters to give highly visible notifications on the indicator board. Plate 15 shows an LCD display and printout.

Other systems incorporate a VDU showing a plan of the area protected using colours to identify the type and location of the event.

10 Examples of control and indicating equipment

a. 3-zone type detection system

Fig. 16.3 illustrates a control unit designed to cover up to 3 zones. It can accept up to 40 heat detectors and 40 smoke detectors per zone and can be fitted with a Remote Signal module for signalling to an RMC or fire brigade control. It can also accept signals from manual call points.

Various coloured LED's indicate the state of each zone and there are key switches for test, reset and silencing alarms.

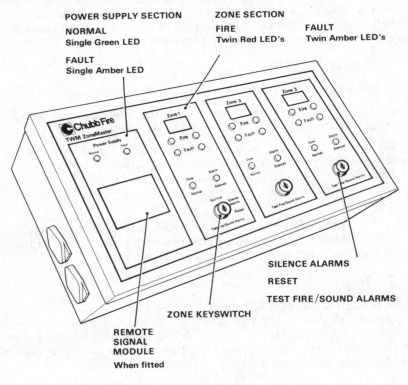

Fig. 16.3 Typical 3-zone control/indicator unit.

In a quiescent condition zone switches are at normal with Power Supply 'normal' and zone 'normal' LED's illuminated. If the power supply fails the supply 'fault' LED is lit and the internal fault sounder activates.

142

(i) Fire condition

When a fire condition is detected the zone alarm circuitry is activated and latched. The alarm sounders operate and the 'fire' condition is indicated by the illumination of the 'fire' LED's. When the key switch on that zone is turned to the 'silence alarm' position the 'fire' LED's remain illuminated, the alarm sounders are silenced and an internal sounder is activated.

(ii) Reset

When all detectors are free from combustion products, expendable fixed temperature detector elements replaced and manual call-points reset; the zone is re-instated to quiescent condition by turning the keyswitch to 'reset' and then to 'normal'.

(iii) Fault

If a detector line is broken, or short-circuited, or a zone fuse fails, the zone fault circuitry is activated and indicated by the illumination of that particular zone 'fault' LED. The internal sounder is activated and the 'normal' LED is extinguished. An open or short circuit fault in an alarm sounder circuit signals a 'fault' condition.

(iv) Other interfaces

This control unit can also be adapted to work in conjunction with an extinguishant control unit capable of meeting BS 5306 Part 4 and 5.1.

b. Multi zone type with microprocessor

Plate 15 illustrates a control unit based on an addressable-analogue concept using a micro-processor, the system conforming to BS5839 Parts 1 and 4. The whole system is 'addressed' every 3 seconds and the replies checked for a 'normal' return. On this particular system 'normal' is given a figure /level of '25'.

(i) Normal level

In a quiescent state the only indicator LED illuminated is 'A.C Healthy' indicating that the power supply is correct. The LCD display will show system normal and alarms '000' see Fig. 16.4.

EVENT LOCATION MESSAGE

	SYSTEM NORMAL	05/11/85
ALARMS:000		11:25:44

Fig. 16.4 Micro-processor indicator board showing system 'Normal'.

(ii)   Pre-alarm level

If a sensor/device reports a transient condition i.e. different from '25', the system logs the event, interrogates the identified device for further data and checks whether it is an alarm condition or only spurious data i.e. electrical interference. If the device returns to a level of '45' a 'pre-alarm' is registered. The 'pre-alarm' LED will illuminate, a warning buzzer sounds, the LCD displays (as shown in Fig. 16.5) and the printer will deliver a printout. The cause of the 'pre-alarm', which could be only a contaminated atmosphere, should be investigated by the person responsible.

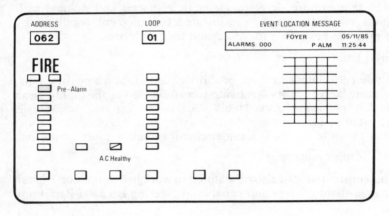

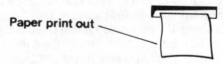

Fig. 16.5 Indicator board registering a pre-alarm signal.

(iii)   Fire level

If a sensor returns a level of '55' then the control unit will decide that there is a fire condition, see Fig. 16.6. The fire LED and particular area LED will illuminate, alarm sounders will operate, to whatever level the system has programmed according to the location of the fire, LCD's will display and the printout will record the event. Other auxiliary systems will be activated e.g. signal to an RMC. If a break glass unit has been operated the 'Manual Alarm' LED is also illuminated.

N.B. The levels of '45' and '55' conform with the required LPC and EN 54 Part 7 Rules.

144

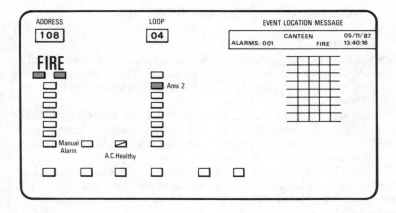

Fig. 16.6 Indicator board registering a fire signal.

(iv)   Fault condition

There are two types of fault condition on the control unit. Where there is a fault on a sensor both the 'monitor fault' and the 'common fault' LED's will illuminate. N.B. The term 'monitor' may be superseded by 'device' or 'sensor'. The fault buzzer will sound and the LCD will display the location and a printout will be received. For any fault on the remainder of the system only the 'common' fault LED will illuminate plus the sounder operating and the LCD printout. In all cases a fire signal will override a fault signal.

(v)   Maintenance

The event store memory of the processor keeps a permanent record of all events and the printout will produce this record on request. This enables an engineer to pinpoint potential trouble areas and, by use of the keypad of the unit, to call-up and test a device as necessary. It can also isolate a device without affecting the remainder of the loop and this will be indicated by an LED, stored in the memory and every 5 minutes a sounder will operate to remind the engineer that the device is isolated.

(vi)   Additional facilities

The control unit can also register, indicate, take appropriate action and record, multiple fire or the spread of fire. It can indicate the need for evacuation whether it be for a real necessity or a drill and will operate alarms, auxiliary outputs etc. as necessary. If following an evacuation the alarms are silenced it will continuously remind the person responsible that the alarms are inoperative until the system is reset.

11 Remote manned centres (RMC's)

a. General

Mention has been made in previous chapters (and see the Manual, Book 10, Chapter 11) to fire alarm systems (FAS) being connected to remote manned centres (RMC) or to local authority fire brigade control rooms.

There are, in a few areas, facilities for FAS to be connected directly to the fire brigade control rooms. For instance, Merseyside Fire Brigade have retained monitoring of FAS in premises within a 30 mile radius of its control room.

Devon Fire and Rescue Service collect FAS signals from data transmitters direct into their command and control computer. Two simple key operations will display the PDA to the premises on the operators screen.

A small area of the country mainly in East Anglia is covered by the 'Alarms by Carrier' (ABC) system. This uses the subscribers normal exchange line onto which is superimposed an inaudible signal. Any failure of this signal is noted by the system together with any 'fire' signal and these are monitored by the brigade. A schematic diagram of the ABC system is shown in Fig. 16.7.

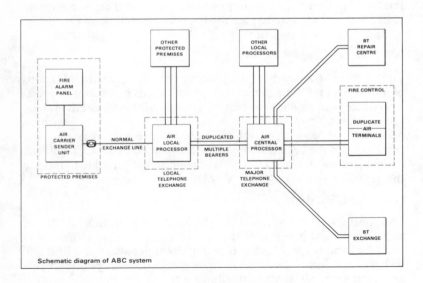

Schematic diagram of ABC system

Fig. 16.7 A schematic diagram of the ABC (Alarms by Carrier) system.

However following the major reorganisation of fire authorities in 1974, most of the original connections between FAS and brigades were discontinued. The fire alarm industry, therefore, had to rapidly expand the number of commercially operated RMCs and update the technology involved. There are, at the moment (1989), no BS/LPC Rules on connections between FAS and RMCs or between RMCs and fire brigade controls but, work is proceeding, mainly with European standards in mind, to formulate guidance.

b. Connections from premises (FAS) to RMCs

There are five distinct means of connection between protected premises and RMCs. These are:-

(i)   Private wires – most RMCs offer this facility;

(ii)   Omnibus circuits – fairly frequent option offered;

(iii)   Connection to RMC satellites – from here signals are multiplexed to the RMC. A number of major companies offer this.

(iv)   Digital communications – widespread facility;

(v)   BTs Red Care system – currently available in a few areas including London.

c. Connections from RMC to fire brigade controls

The means by which RMCs pass calls to fire brigade controls come into four categories and these are:-

(i)   Private wires;

(ii)   999 facilities – either with or outside the RMC area;

(iii)   Ex-directory numbers of fire brigade control rooms

(iv)   Use of normal administrative brigade telephone numbers.

The permutations of both (b) and (c) are shown in Fig. 16.8.

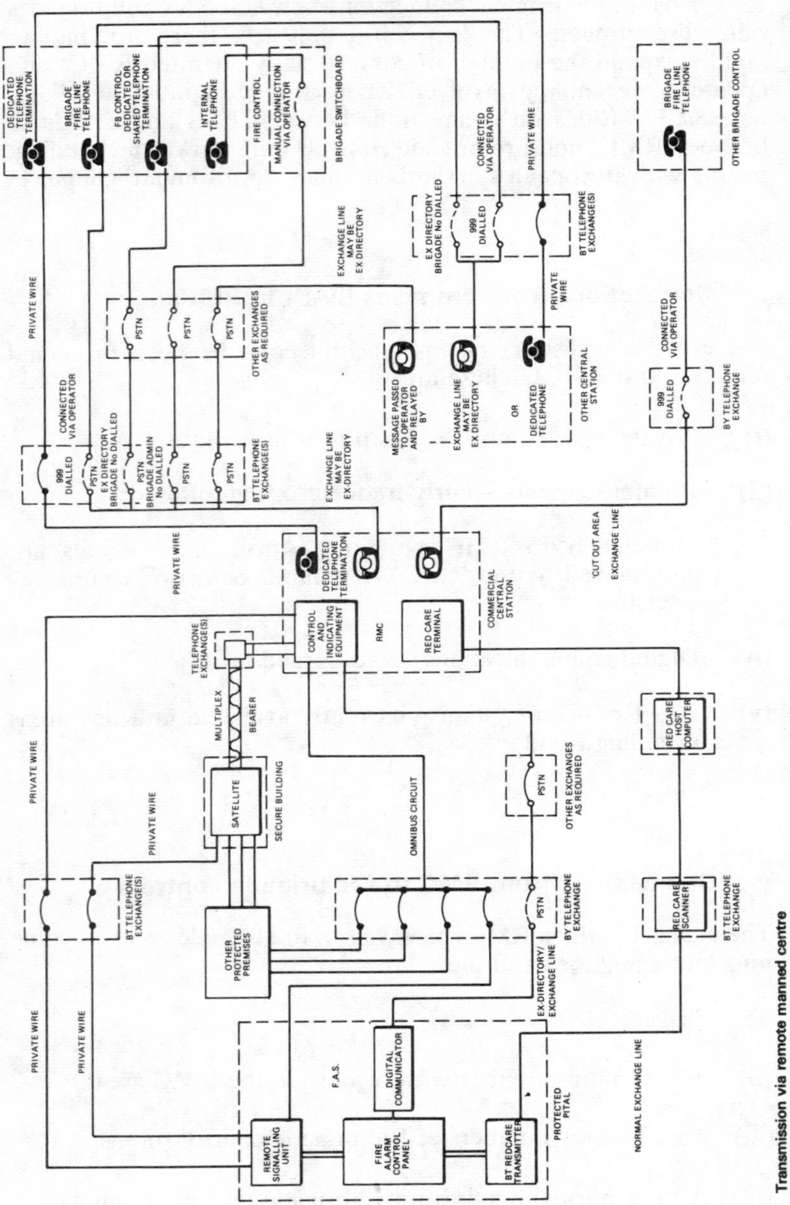

Fig. 16.8 The various means by which RMCs can transmit call to the fire
brigade controls.

d. **Methods of transmission – protected premises to RMC**

(i)   Private wire

A dedicated and continuously monitored path via a telephone exchange, not necessarily a unique pair of wires but more usually part of a multiplex circuit which, over long distances, could be transmitted by microwave. BT provides most of the circuits but Mercury also carry traffic. Economically often limited to 10–15 km radius.

(ii)   Omnibus circuits

In this system a number of premises share a communications path. Each premises has a dedicated spur connection to a telephone exchange from where there is a single circuit to the RMC. Due to line losses the number of premises on any one line are limited but it is economical over relatively long distances. Each premises is scanned together with the others but the code transmitted by the RMC only elicits an answer from one e.g. current state 'normal', 'fault' or 'fire'.

(iii)   RMC satellites

A satellite is a form of data concentrator to which premises can be connected either by private wire of omnibus circuit. It is virtually an unmanned RMC into which a large number of signals can be received and re-transmitted to an RMC, collecting data from a number of satellites. There is an added advantage that, if communications break down between a satellite and the RMC, the satellite can be manned although the multiplex systems are usually backed up by a duplication or by switching to the PSTN using modems.

(iv)   Digital communications (DC)

This is a signalling device that is connected to an exchange telephone line. In the event of a fire signal operating at the premises the DC dials up the RMC using the PSTN. A receiver at the RMC answers and a series of coded tones is sent by the DC, decoded by the RMC receiver and displayed on the operators VDU for action. The advantage of this system is that there is no limit to distance of transmission and it is economic. The disadvantage is that, any congestion on the PSTN, and the signal may not go through however many times the DC is programmed to dial.

(v)   BT Red Care

This is a system similar in principle to ABC but whereas ABC utilises the telephone supply current, the power supply for the care transmitter (known as a Subscriber Terminal Unit (STU)) is derived from the FAS.

Two forms of signalling are involved (a) a continuous monitoring signal which is on an inaudible frequency generated and 'recognised' by the scanner (equivalent to the local processor in ABC) and (b) a continuous poll of each STU by the scanner which responds with alarm status conditions.

e. Methods of transmission

(i) Private wire

Here the RMC resets a private circuit from a public telecommunications operator e.g. BT and this terminates in a brigade control. This makes a highly reliable connection but even this is usually backed up by a secondary method in case of failure.

(ii) 999 facilities

If the RMC and protected premises happen to be located in the same area, a 999 call from the RMC will usually be connected by BT, to the fire brigade control covering that area. Arrangements can, with additional expense, be made to use the 999 system via an 'out-of-area' exchange line if the protected premises is in a different area to the RMC.

The disadvantage of using the 999 system is the human link i.e. the BT operator which could slow down the transmission of the call.

(iii) Ex-directory number

A number of brigades provide an RMC with an ex-directory telephone number that permits access via the PSTN, to their control room and there the call is recognised as an emergency call. However, any use of the PSTN leaves a line susceptible to faults or even congestion and can cause delays in transmission.

(iv) Administrative telephone number

This method is probably the most unacceptable although it is not unknown. There can be very significant delays in answering such calls which have a low priority in any brigade control. It may even have to pass through a separate administrative switchboard before reaching the control; the line itself might be engaged; there may be a fault on the line or the PSTN may be congested.

Chapter 17
Detector positioning

1 General

As pointed out in the introduction to this part, a great deal of thought is required when designing an AFD system. Reference must be made to British Standards and the relevant ones are listed below.

BS 5445 Pt.5 Heat sensitive detectors
BS 5445 Pt.7 Smoke detectors
BS 5445 Pt.8 High temperature heat detectors
BS 5446 Pt.1 Point type smoke detectors
BS 5839 Pt.1 Code of practice for system design installation and servicing
BS 5839 Pt.4 Control and indicating equipment
BS 5839 Pt.5 Specification for optical beam detectors
BS 6266 Fire protection for electronic data processing installations.

Two other publications have a bearing in the subject:–

(i)   Loss Prevention Council (LPC) 'Recommendations for the protection of computer installations against fire'

Table 13. A general division of types of detector for the type of risk covered.

	DETECTOR TYPE				
	Heat	Ionization	Optical	Flame	Beam
USE FOR	Dusty, smokey areas. Smokeless fires.	Flaming Fires General purpose application.	Smouldering fires. Areas with air movement.	Flammable gases. Explosion risks. Smokeless fires.	Ducts. Large open areas Corridors
EXAMPLES	Sub-stations Generators Remote locations	Offices Hotels Computer Rooms	Electrical cables and machinery Plastics Air Conditioned Areas Computer Rooms	Alcohol fires. Hydrocarbons fires.	Warehouses Computer rooms.
RESPONSE SPEED	SLOW	FAST	FAST	VERY FAST	FAST
DO NOT USE FOR	Low heat fires Smouldering fires	Dusty areas Areas with high air velocity	Dusty areas	Smokey fires Areas with obstructions which would interfere with line of sight of the detector	Dusty areas Areas with obstructions Areas with constant maintenance obstructing beam.

(ii)   DHSS Technical Memorandum 'Fire safety in health care premises. Detection and alarm systems'.

The description of the capabilities of various types of detectors (see previous chapters) indicate that, under given conditions, certain types will have a better rate of detection. Table 13 gives a general division of types according to the sort of risk covered. In the relevant British Standards, depending on location and general type of detector used, certain distances and operational areas are stipulated. Building configurations are taken into consideration and Table 14 gives a general summary of the detector positioning and requirement and advice. Most systems use zones and this must be borne in mind because there are limitations on the areas which can be covered by any one zone (see Chapter 16 section 2).

Table 14. A general summary of detector positioning and requirements.

DETECTOR POSITIONING				
	Smoke		Heat	
	In General	Corridors	In General	Corridors
Area per detector	100m^2		50m^2	
Max. detector separation.	12m	18m	10m	15m
Max. detector distance from any point	7m	9m	5m	7.5m
Max. detector height	10.5m		6m (Grade 3) 7.5m (Grade 2) 9m (Grade 1)	
Distance from roof obstruction.	.60m		.60m	
Distance from wall	.50m		.50m	
Distance from air inlets	1.5m		1.5m	
Perforated Ceilings	Blank off 1m^2 of perforated ceiling above detector.		Blank off 1m^2 of perforated ceiling above detector.	
Airflow	Mount in areas of normal air circulation. Note effects of airflow.		Mount out of airflow.	
Beams	Beams more than 0.1 of room height are considered to create separate compartments.		Mount in area between beams Also see opposite.	
Racks	Racks reaching to within .30m of ceiling create separate compartments.		See opposite.	
Sloping Roof	Mount detector in apex of roof.		See opposite.	

There are, however, very much stricter recommendations for areas of very high value risk e.g. electronic data processing (EDP) rooms. Here detector density can be as high as 15m^2 or, in extreme cases, one detector or sensing point actually inside a cabinet.

Due regard must be given to the capability of the detector selected and what, if any, local conditions obtain which may confuse that particular type. Change of use of a building that, if not actually nullifying the usefulness of the detectors, could give rise to false alarms or, worse, late alarms. Recent work on protecting escape routes has shown that the standards originally laid down in BS 5839 Pt.1 (1982 amendment) were inadequate. The Code now recommends that, to give satisfactory protection on escape routes, detectors should be installed both on the escape route and in adjoining rooms. In the rooms a smoke or heat detector mounted either on the ceiling or on the wall above door level should be adequate.

2   Smoke detectors

a.   General

The ability of a detector to detect smoke particles depends on air movement and the height of the detector above the source of smoke. This has to be considered against the configuration of the compartment protected, possible obstructions, types of contents involved, requirements of legislation etc. BS 5839 Pt.1 limits the area covered by a smoke detector to $100m^2$. In general, the distance from any point to the nearest detector should not exceed 7.5m (but see 2h below). A height limit of 10.5m also applies except where a system is connected to an approved remote manned control (RMC) or brigade control and the brigade can attend within 5 minutes. Under these conditions the height limit can be raised to 15m.

b.   Heat inversion

Another problem, especially in single storey buildings, is the tendency for a layer of warm air to accumulate near, or at, ceiling level, This can prevent smoke rising to the detector and consideration needs to be given to suspending the detector heads below the likely level of this warm layer.

c.   Air movement

Detectors should be placed in the path of the normal air flow and this includes artificial ventilation because smoke can originate from outside the area. Care must be taken, however, not to place them too close to a fresh air flow. Figs. 17.1 and 17.2 show examples of positioning. For instance, an intake down through a perforated ceiling can make it difficult to protect as smoke would tend to be pushed downwards. However, an additional detector near the outlet would cover that point.

Constant air movement by, for instance, artificial ventilation, can prevent smoke reaching a detector and it can also affect the sensitivity of ionisation type detectors. Usually the solution is to compensate, either by reducing the area each detector monitors or increasing their sensitivity.

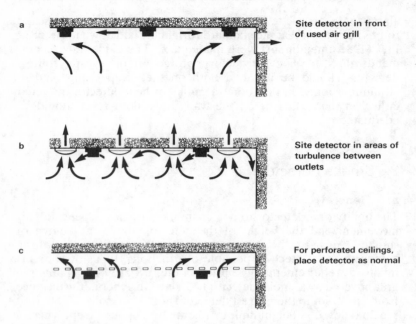

Fig. 17.1 Examples of positioning of detectors where flow of air is out of the building or compartment.

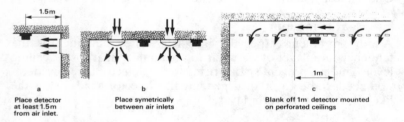

Fig. 17.2 Examples of detector positioning where flow of air is into the building or compartment.

d.   Voids

The increasing designed use of voids, both ceiling and underfloor, poses another problem. If they are less than 800mm in height they need not be protected unless:–

(i)   spread of fire of smoke can take place between rooms of compartments by that route;

(ii)   power cables are contained therein;

(iii) they are adjacent to a high risk area.

154

Any detectors sited in voids should be hung downwards to prevent dust accumulating on them. Any use of voids by ventilation systems would create fast air-flows and the type of detection should be as for ducts (see section 2(i)).

Another construction which gives rise to what are, technically, voids although not in the strictly closed sense, is the common use of grids suspended from ceilings. Tests have shown that any construction of this kind made of small squares or parallels with small gaps, has a significant effect on smoke travel. Any grid ceilings with spaces less than 0.2m wide will act as a smoke barrier and the space above should be treated as a void..

e. Walls, beams and galleries

Positioning detectors within certain distances of walls or beams could put them into 'dead' air space where there may be little or no air flow. Beams less than 0.15m deep can be ignored but any beam more than 0.1 of the height of the compartment should be treated as a separating wall for smoke travel purposes.

A gallery or small mezzanine will require special consideration and the BS illustrates the formula which should be applied generally in these cases.

f. Corridors

In a corridor, or a small room with a width of 2m or less, detectors can be spaced at 18m intervals. This, however, may have to be modified if a particular corridor forms part of a means of escape (see section 1 General).

g. Staircases, shafts etc.

In a staircase or shaft at least one detector should be placed on the top floor ceiling. If any of the lower floors are separated from upper floors by a smoke barrier e.g. fire door, then an extra detector must be installed in the ceiling in front of this barrier.

Generally one detector may not monitor more than three floors of a staircase. Additional detectors may not monitor more than three floors of a staircase. Additional detectors may be required on very high staircases (see Fig. 17.3).

In a shaft one detector every 18m vertically is the minimum.

h. Sloping ceilings and roofs

Smoke tends to concentrate in the apex of a sloping room and this enables extra distance to be allowed from any point to the nearest detector. This amounts to 1 per cent for every 1 degree of the slope of the roof. For example, with a 20 degree slope of roof detectors mounted in the apex can cover 7.5m (general maximum) × 20/100 = 1.5. Distance to the nearest detector from any point can,

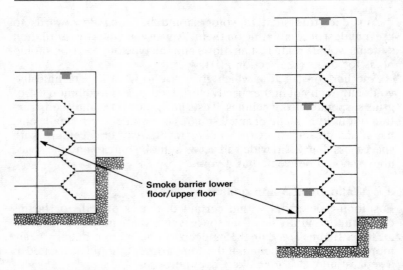

Fig. 17.3 Detector positioning on a staircase.

therefore, be $7.5 + 1.5m = 9m$. Therefore total maximum permissible distance between detectors becomes 18m.

Slopes of roofs and ceilings are not always uniform and where a detector cannot be positioned in the apex it should be mounted on the part of the ceiling with the least slope and as close to the apex as possible. The detector density may need to be modified as a result.

i.   Duct

Duct protection presents a problem usually because of very fast air flows. The following types of smoke detector can be used:–

(1)   Beam detector

(2)   Ionisation duct detector

(3)   Optical detector

(4)   Air sampling systems

These types all have advantages and disadvantages as shown in Table 13. In addition the very fast air flow:

(i)   precludes the use of an ionisation detector if the flow is above 4m/s as this affects the sensitivity of the detector;

(ii)   tends to be stratified and follows a particular channel within the duct;

(iii)   dilutes the measurable smoke.

This means that the choice of detector system will depend a lot on the width of the duct and the rate of smoke generation. Detectors, especially air sampling apparatus, should be carefully placed for maximum efficiency. Positioning will, among other things, depend on avoiding areas of turbulence and places where smoke could be diluted, e.g. junctions with others ducts.

j.   Electronic data processing (EDP) installations

Reference has already been made to the extra protection considered necessary for EDP and other types of very high value risks. Most, if not all, have very sophisticated air conditioning systems, cable ducts, floor and ceiling voids, fast-acting extinguishing systems etc. The detection system must be able to prevent too many false alarms. It may also have to trigger other systems, e.g. to close-down or reverse ventilation, shut-down machinery, protect power supplies to a computer and give sufficient warning of a halon release to the occupants. BS 6226 recommends that the type of detectors used should be of the highest sensitivity and the concentration of the detectors enough to detect the smallest fires quickly. The BS also recommends the accurate zoning of the various areas at risk.

3   Heat detectors

a.   General

Heat detectors are, usually, much slower in their reaction than smoke detectors but they are very reliable, require the minimum of maintenance and rarely give false alarms. In the UK, BS 5445 Parts 5 and 8 require that all such detectors have a maximum temperature response whether they are rate-of-rise or fixed temperature types. The BS also grades detectors according to their operating temperatures which, in each case, have to be between a lower and upper limit. The lower limit is to prevent ambient temperatures from causing false alarms and the upper limit ensures an adequate speed of response. The detectors are colour coded as follows:

Grade	Colour
Grade 1	Green
Grade 2	Yellow
Grade 3	Red

BS 5445 Part 5 page 3 gives the response times according to grade and the response temperatures for all grades when the rate of rise of air temperature is less than 10°C/min.

157

b. Positioning

With a few exceptions, the considerations for positioning heat detectors are the same as for smoke detectors. The exceptions are:–

(i)   Height

Heat intensity decreases rapidly as distance increase which means that the height limits are lower than those for smoke detectors. In each grade of detector (see a. above) there is a maximum higher limit height and a maximum general limit height. The higher limits are applicable where a brigade can make an attendance within 5 minutes. For example, this means that a grade 2 detector will have a higher height limit of 12m and a general height limit of 7.5m.

However, for maximum temperature heat detectors, as described in BS 5445 Part 8, the higher limit height is 10.5m and the general height limit is 6m.

In contrast to smoke detectors, heat detectors should be sited so that the element is not more than 50mm below the ceiling. It will determine whether heat detectors can be used.

(ii)   Area

The maximum area to be covered by a heat detector is $50m^2$ and the maximum distance allowed from any point to the nearest detector is 5.3m giving a detector separation of 10.6m. In corridors, this can be increased to 13.6m (but see section 1, General).

(iii)   Sloping ceilings
        The detector should be sited in the apex of the roof.

(iv)   Beams and similar construction
        The detector should be mounted on the ceiling only in the interbeam area.

Chapter 18
Manually-operated fire alarms

In the introduction of Part 2 the point was made that a fire alarm can be raised automatically by a detection system or manually by a person in the affected building. This Chapter examines the latter method. Such an alarm will generally be either wholly manual or manual/electric, not forgetting that an alarm can always be raised vocally.

1 Manual systems

The purely manual means for raising an alarm involves the use of basic devices which include the following:

(i)   Rotary gongs which are sounded by simply leading the handle around the rim of the gong

(ii)   Hand strikers e.g. iron triangles suspended from a wall accompaned by a metal bar which is used to strike the triangle and produce a loud clanging noise

(iii)   Handbells

(iv)   Whistles.

These devices are normally found in a readily available location on the walls of corridors, entrance halls and staircase landings.

They are relatively cheap and while they give an alarm over a limited area, are rarely adequate to give a general alarm throughout the premises; nor do they necessarily convey the alarm to a central point from which the fire brigade can be speedily summoned.

As a person is required to operate them a continuous alarm cannot be guaranteed for as long as may be necessary.

Because of these restrictions in their use it is unlikely that these devices will be the sole means of raising alarms except perhaps in low risk areas.

2 Manual/electric systems

These are systems which, although set in motion manually, operate as part of an electrical circuit. Manual call points, as they are known, can be incorporated with detectors into a comprehensive fire alarm system which allows for automatic and/or manual raising of an alarm.

The call points in a manual/electric system are invariably small, wall mounted boxes as shown in Plate 16. They are designed to operate either:

(i)   automatically, when the glass front is broken, or

(ii)   when the glass front is broken AND the button pressed in.

The majority of available models are designed to operate immediately the glass front is broken.

Contact (1) (Fig. 18.1) is connected to one side of the electrical circuit, and contact (2) to the other. The movement of contact (1) is governed by the spring loaded button which is maintained in the depressed position by the glass front. Normally, therefore, contact (1) is held off contact (2), but once the glass is broken, the spring forces the button outwards, allowing contact (1) to engage with contact (2) thus completing an electrical circuit and raising the alarm.

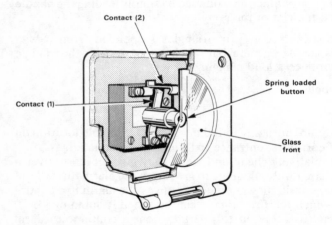

Fig. 18.1 An illustration of a fire-alarm call point.

As an alternative this type of call-point can be fitted so that the electrical circuit is normally complete, a relay being incorporated to hold off the alarm. On breaking the glass the circuit is broken, the relay de-energises and the alarm sounds.

In either case, accidental breaking of the glass will, of course, raise a false alarm. This is most likely to happen in a situation where various goods and materials are being moved about (e.g. in workshops and storage areas). This problem can be overcome by installing a call-point in which the button has to be manually pressed in to raise the alarm after the glass has been broken. When the button is released the alarm will continue to sound.

To help with the breaking of glass in call-points most manufacturers will provide, if requested, a small chromium-plated hammer for attaching by chain to the box. In place of the hammer some manufacturers will 'score' a circle in the glass for easier breakage; this enables it to be broken by a blow with the tips of the fingers. Obviously these arrangements are desirable only when the possibility of accidental or malicious breaking is minimal.

Where neither hammer nor scored glass is available a blow with a covered elbow, a shoe heel or other sharp object will be effective.

In certain types of occupancy (e.g. mental health units) or in situations where vandalism is likely, a modified call point is often fitted and these points have a solid door with a keyhole. When the key is inserted and turned the electric circuit is completed and an alarm is raised. The key will normally be in the possession of, or accessible to, authorised personnel only.

Recommendations on the installation of manual call points are given in BS 5839 Pt.2. In general terms they should obviously be fitted in conspicuous positions, usually on escape routes, where anyone operating them is not exposed to undue risk.

3 Miscellaneous

In addition to the facilities specifically designed for raising an alarm it may be possible to use general communication facilities e.g. a telephone or public address system.

With automatic telephone systems arrangements can be made for a particular dialling code to be reserved for use when reporting a fire. Use of such a code will connect the caller to a person (normally the operator) responsible for calling the fire brigade and sounding the general alarm; alternatively it can be arranged that use of the code automatically sounds the general alarm and/or calls the brigade.

While such systems are useful as 'back-up' services it can be unwise to rely on them as the sole means of raising an alarm. They may have the two main disadvantages of delay:

(a)   in contacting the person at the switchboard or public address system;

(b)   the further delay that can occur between this contact and the actual raising of the general alarm.

4 Restricted alarms

In order to avoid unnecessary disturbance in hospitals and other larger installations, it may be desirable to restrict an initial alarm to the locality in which it arises, or to a small number of restricted personnel. A general alarm would then be sounded only if a 'duty officer' considered it desirable to do so.

Signal light systems which are often installed for summoning staff for various purposes, can be used for restricted alarms; operation of the call point producing a certain light code signal. These lights may be installed at hospital ward entrances, passage intersections and other places where they are conspicuous to staff.

Restricted alarm systems must have a control point which is under continuous and competent watch during the whole time the premises are occupied. An overriding switch should also be provided to enable the 'duty officer' or other responsible person to raise a general alarm for complete evacuation. In all cases it is essential to ensure that the fire brigade have been called. Firefighters should make themselves aware of the various types of systems in their area.

Part 3
Fire Venting Systems

Operational fire venting is dealt with in the Manual, Book 12, Part 3 but this Part of Book 9 examines Ventilation systems which form a structural part of a building and they are considered in two groups:

(i)   Single-storey buildings

Here the reasons for having fire-venting systems i.e. the reduction of fire spread and prevention of smoke-logging, and the advantage this gives to firefighters in controlling the fire, are discussed. Sometimes these fitted systems double as both health and fire ventilation.

(ii)   Multi-storey buildings

Most ventilation systems in this type of building are fitted for health purposes and, in a lot of cases, are a positive disadvantage under fire conditions. Chapter 21 describes the systems installed and the measures designed into them to stop the spread of products of combustion through a building.

Chapter 19
Ventilation in Single Storey Buildings

In fire conditions it is generally accepted that correct ventilation reduces firespread, smoke-logging and resultant damage, and also enables firefighters to enter a building more easily. There are many large single storey buildings in this country with unprotected roof trussing, few, if any, interior walls and spacious open storage or production areas. Ventilation systems have been fitted to many such buildings and, on occasions, have successfully reduced fire losses.

1 Purposes of venting

a. Prevention of Smoke Logging

Venting allows smoke and other products of combustion to leave the building making a relatively cool clear atmosphere beyond the immediate fire area (Fig. 19.1). The increased visibility helps firefighters to locate the seat of the fire and the release of the products of combustion also eliminates the explosion risk of partially burnt gases.

Early venting also has the effect of providing added oxygen for more complete combustion which assists the prevention of smoke-logging. This is most easily achieved by an automatically controlled

NO VENTING

Can be smoke logged
within 5 minutes of outbreak

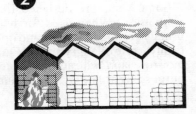

WITH VENTING & SCREENS

Remains clear of smoke
until extinguished

Fig. 19.1 Adequate venting allows combustion products to leave the building. The effect: (1) with no venting. (2) with venting and screens.

165

system. In a small building the effect is immediate while in a large building it is only as the fire develops that venting provides the oxygen necessary for complete combustion.

Besides preventing smoke logging, automatic controls are also favoured because:

(i)   there may be problems in reaching manual controls in fire conditions;

(ii)   they provide for the possibility of earlier detection by a passer-by when the building is unoccupied

(iii)   they may also be adapted to signal to a local control eg a gatehouse or an RMC (see Chapter 21)

b. Prevention of spread of fire

Mushrooming (the high-level spread of gases and smoke) is checked by early ventilation thus preventing pre-heating of other areas by convection and also restricting the spread of fire). Ventilation also cuts down on the area of roof damage away from the fire by reducing the sideways spread of flame beneath the ceiling. Damage is obviously greater over the immediate fire area but proportionally less at a distance from the fire. Reducing the temperature generally at roof level helps to prevent, or delay, softening of the steel framework of the building (this occurs at approx 500°C) which could mean early collapse of the roof and, perhaps, walls.

2   Specific use of fire ventilators

Ventilators fitted in buildings for health purposes may well vent the products of combustion when there is a fire. The ventilators examined in this chapter are those fitted to buildings *primarily* for fire venting purposes.

Some vents are designed for the dual role of fire and health ventilation. When used for health purposes such ventilators are usually grouped together and operated by mechanically or pneumatically controlled systems. One type has a device sensitive to moisture and will automatically close when it rains. In all dual purpose ventilators a fire alarm signal will override any such switches.

3   Vent construction

Most vents are designed with opening doors or pivoted louvres. Steel or anodised aluminium are used for the doors whilst louvres are generally of aluminium or polycarbonate and the opening mechanism is usually operated by a fire detector.

Some vents are merely closed by a polythene-based plastic sheet which has a relatively low melting point. When softened by the heat of a fire the sheet of plastic falls from its mounting leaving the vent open.

4 Vent operation

Both heat and smoke detectors are used for automatic vent control.

a. Heat detectors

The simplest and most common method of detection used is the fusible link. The time for reaction depends on its size, shape, material and position. The link is usually shielded from sprinkler discharge so that the cooling effect of the water does not delay its action (Fig. 19.2).

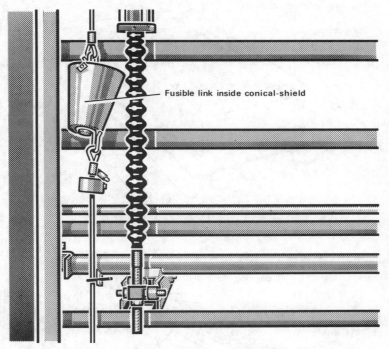

Fusible link inside conical-shield

Fig. 19.2 Part of a roof ventilator (louvre type) showing heat detector.

b. Smoke detectors

These are used as a back-up to fusible links in very high buildings. Hot air rising to a great height may cool so that fusing temperatures are not reached but, when smoke has collected in the roof, smoke detectors will operate the venting system instead.

5 Vent position

Vent efficiency is largely dependent on position. Vents should ideally be at the highest point in each control area, usually the apex of the roof. They are sited so that the suction effect produced by the wind aids the flow of hot gases.

Sometimes the pressure on windward slopes with steep patches tends to force cold air into the building producing smoke logging. For these difficult positions roof ventilators have been designed with electrically driven fans to overcome the air pressure (see Plate 20). Wiring, switch-gear and motors have to be specially designed to withstand high temperatures.

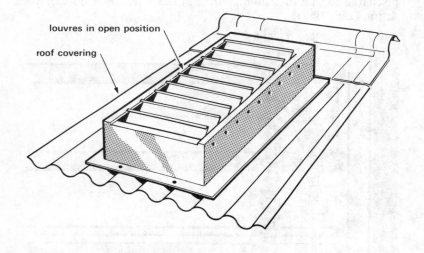

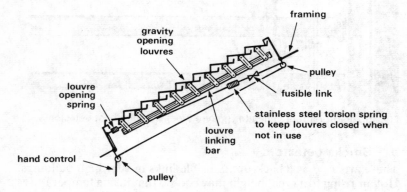

Fig. 19.3 Louvred fire ventilator.

It is generally advantageous to have, in preference to one large vent, a number of small ones distributed evenly over the roof (Fig. 19.3). The exposure hazard to other buildings is thereby decreased since the height of flames emerging from the vents is smaller.

6   Area of venting

If vents have a lower softening temperature than the rest of the roof e.g. plastic roof vents, Building Regulations recommend their area and position in relation to the boundary.

Vents which have the same ability to resist fire as the rest of the roof however are not covered separately by Building Regulations. In this case ventilation requirements depend not on the size of the building but on the following interconnected factors:

(i)   the assumed size of the fire

(ii)   the depth of the layer of hot gases or the minimum height for the layer of cool air;

(iii)   the subdivision of the roof space;

(iv)   the general intention to keep the temperature of hot gases below approximately 200°C.

7   Air inlets

So far in this chapter ventilation has mostly been considered as the exhaustion of the products of combustion. In fact it is the provision of adequate inlets which dictates the efficiency of any ventilation system.

Cold air generally flows into a building by natural means – leaks round doors, windows and other apertures. These inlets must be generally below the expected level of hot air and, ideally, as near the floor as possible. If the inlets are not low enough cold air may entrain hot gases and result in smoke logging at ground level. An exception to this general rule, however, is the situation shown in Fig. 19.5 and described in Section 8 below.

It is recommended that the area of air inlets should at least equal the total area of roof vents. A higher ratio is desirable for premises housing goods which cause smoky fires without reaching high temperatures.

8   Other factors

In reality it is impossible to consider ventilation in isolation. There are several factors which influence the effectiveness of a venting system. The most important ones are:

(a)   the sub-division of the roof space with screens

(b)   the sub-division of the floor area with smoke or fire curtains

(c)   the position of sprinklers.

a.   Screens

Subdividing the roof space with screens is known to considerably increase the efficiency of vents, and was mentioned as one of the factors affecting the area of ventilators required.

(1)   Screen construction

Screens are constructed of materials which are as resistant to the effects of fire as the roof (not necessarily non-combustible). They need to be reasonably gas-tight although small leaks where pipes pass through are not of great importance particularly when low down.

Screens are generally placed at right angles to a pitched roof (Fig. 19.4), dividing the roof into compartments about 45–60 metres apart. This varies according to the factory or storage layout, since screens positioned over spaces between goods, tend to reduce fire spread.

It is the depth of the screens which governs the time before hot air spills into adjacent compartments. Screens should, ideally, reach as near the floor as possible to prevent fire spread by radiation. In practice they often only reach down as far as truss tie level as shown in Fig. 19.4.

Some screens are constructed so that in normal conditions they are retracted near the roof and, under fire conditions, they fall on operation of fusible links.

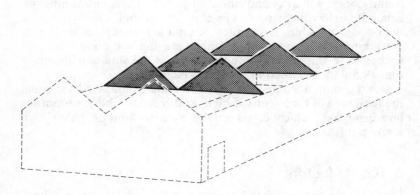

Fig. 19.4 A diagrammatic example of screens dividing a roof space.

(2) Screen effect

If a roof is divided into compartments by screens the area above the fire fills with hot gases first. The local temperature is increased and this significantly improves the response time of automatic roof vents.

The lateral flow of smoke is restricted so that the roof vents in a non smoke-logged part of the building can be opened manually to allow the air to flow (Fig. 19.5).

When used in conjunction with sprinklers, screens restrict water damage by preventing or reducing the activation of sprinkler heads away from the source of the fire.

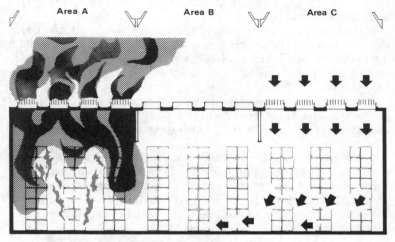

Area A   Area B   Area C

WAREHOUSE BUILDING WITH LIMITED DOOR OPENING.

When fire vents over Area C are opened cool air falls to the floor, drifts towards the fire and allows vents over the hot area to exhaust at full capacity.
System maintains safe condition for fire fighting and avoids unnecessary damage by smoke and blind use of water.

Fig. 19.5 A warehouse with limited door openings–ventilation being improved by the opening of vents in a cool area.

b.   Smoke and fire curtains

(1)   Smoke curtains

These are very similar to screens but usually reach the floor to make a completely enveloped area. Some are semi-permanently fixed like light partition walls, others are designed to unroll into position automatically on the operation of AFDs or fire alarms. They restrict spread of smoke and hot gases and tend to complement the smoke-venting system.

(2)   Fire curtains

Fire curtains are designed to contain fire and have been tested to over a 2-hour rating. The *Manual*, Book 8, Chapter 10 refers to their requirement to be fitted between stage and auditorium in a conventional theatre. They were made of asbestos cloth, but are now mainly fibreglass with stainless steel wire reinforcing.

Another use of fire curtains is to compartment hangar decks on R.N. ships in the event of fire.

c.   Sprinklers

Sprinklers themselves influence the effectiveness of a ventilation system and there is much debate as to whether sprinklers or ventilators should operate first.

If sprinklers operate *before* vents, rising smoke may be cooled thereby delaying the opening of vents and, at worst, causing them not to operate at all. This cooling effect may also cause the smoke to sink to the ground, reducing visibility and so hinder the efforts of firefighters.

If sprinklers operate *after* vents, the escaping heat may retard their early operation. However, this does restrict the opening of sprinklers away from the fire, which in turn prevents unnecessary water damage.

There are various opinions as to whether sprinklers or ventilators should operate first – latest reports from brigades in the United Kingdom show no cases where venting has made control of sprinkled fires difficult. It is fairly obvious that a combined sprinkled-venting system must be 'tailored' to a particular building and the particular use and contents.

9   Additional controls

Under certain circumstances at a fire it may be necessary to open vents before the operating temperature of the automatic system is reached. Many installations have a 'Firefighters override control' which can be manually operated to open all vents it is connected to, overriding any other control. This 'override' can also be used for test purposes by the engineer or local fire authority.

In a fire situation it would, obviously, be wise to have firefighting equipment laid out ready before operating the override.

Rain sensitive switches (see Section 2 above) would also be overridden by the manual control.

Chapter 20
Smoke Control in Shopping Complexes

1 General

Fires in shopping complexes and the problems of smoke hazarding means of escape have provoked a great deal of thought. The malls, associated squares, common areas etc. which make up the main public concourses would, naturally, be the means which the public would use for escape in the event of a fire in one of the adjoining shops. It follows, therefore, that these areas must be kept as smoke-free as possible in such an event. It is generally accepted that, by their very nature, the shops or units opening onto the malls etc. constitute the main fire risks. In a fire the hot smoky gases (HSG) will pass out of the shop and rise to the mall ceiling mixing with fresh air as they go. Without smoke control measures, HSG will flow along a mall, as a ceiling layer, at a speed typically between 1 and 2 m/s. This is probably faster than the escape speed of pedestrians in a crowded mall. If HSG reach a closed end of a mall they will drop to a low level and be drawn back towards the fire. As an example, an unsprinkled fire in a single storey shopping centre is judged to have caused a 100m mall to become untenable in about one minute.

2 Basic Principles of Control

As a general principle air will mix into a rising stream of HSG but will not mix appreciably into a horizontally flowing stream except under special conditions. In a multi-storey mall the higher HSG rise the greater amount of air becomes entrained and mixed, leading to a much larger volume of cooler smoky gases reaching the upper ceiling layer. The problem here is how to control and remove the HSG before they cool and fall to the level of people in the upper walkways of the mall (Fig. 20.1).

As a result of research, the Fire Research Station recommend control of lateral spread of HSG across the ceiling by screens or upstands. Those should be of sufficient depth (not less than 2m) to contain HSG in a 'reservoir' from which they can be removed. Screens/upstands can be either permanent features of the structure

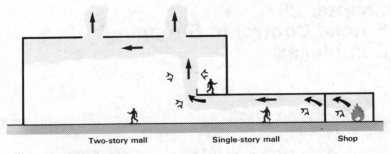

Fig. 20.1 Probable smoke travel in a multi-storey shopping mall.

or actuated by automatic fire detectors. Examples are illustrated in Figs. 20.2, 20.3, 20.4 and 20.5 and also Plates 21 and 22.

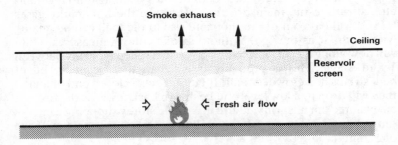

Fig. 20.2 Diagram showing a mall fitted with smoke reservoir screens and ventilators.

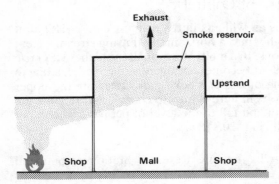

Fig. 20.3 Diagram showing how a built-in upstand acts as a smoke reservoir.

174

HSG contained in a reservoir will lose heat by downward radiation and heat transfer to walls and ceilings. To ensure that people can escape below the HSG the base of the layer should be maintained at least 3m above their heads in a single-storey mall and the same distance above their heads in an upper walkway. In order to achieve this, FRS recommend that the horizontal area of reservoirs should be limited to about 1000m². This should ensure that the HSG retain their buoyancy whilst being removed. Ideally the maximum distance anybody has to travel under a HSG layer should be about 60m and reservoir boundaries should be sited midway between the pedestrian exits provided in mall sections. This may be difficult to arrange where the reservoirs are upstands as the reservoir 'boundary' then becomes blurred but a sensible decision erring on the side of safety should be taken.

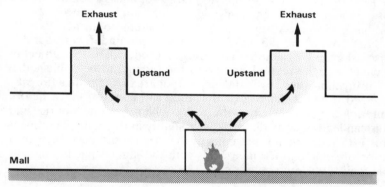

Fig. 20.4 Another example of designed upstands acting as smoke reservoir.

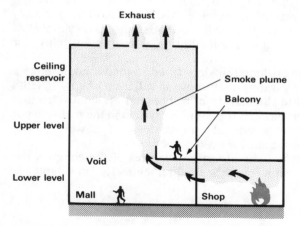

Fig. 20.5 An atrium being used as a smoke reservoir.

3 Removal of hot smoky gases

HSG can be removed from the reservoirs either by natural means or by mechanical extraction. The rate of exhaust must equal the probable rate at which HSG will enter the reservoir from below. Fresh air must enter the mall also at a rate equal to the rate of extraction and low enough not to prematurely mix with (and cool) the HSG. The siting of the exit points where the HSG leave the building needs consideration to avoid creating a hazard elsewhere.

In two-storey malls any natural buoyancy-driven venting is very easily disturbed by external wind pressure because of the cooler smoky gas temperature. FRS therefore recommend mechanical extraction in these cases (see Plate 20). It is obvious that in malls of 3 or more storeys smoke control measures will become progressively more difficult because of the very large volumes of relatively cool smoky gases. In such cases advice on smoke control should probably tend more towards that appertaining to atria.

N.B. Atria, at the time of writing, are under considerable discussion and, as a modern building method, will be the subject of a chapter in the revised Book 8 of the Manual to be published.

In any unit (shop) over $1000m^2$ in floor area HSG from a fire may need to travel so far to exit that they will cool too much before entering the mall. Mixing with fresh cool air they may not rise and this can lead to immediate loss of visibility in the mall. To prevent this FRS recommend that units of this size should have their own reservoirs and extraction systems with the same capacity limits as the mall.

4 Sprinklers

It is considered that a typical flow of HSG at a high enough temperature to set off a sprinkler head will not be seriously disturbed by the spray until the fire is diminishing. This should not cause problems for the public but may reduce visibility for firefighters.

One suggestion is that sprinklers fitted in malls should have a higher temperature rating than those in adjacent shops. If HSG does penetrate into the mall from a shop and are controlled and extracted by reservoirs etc. the sprinkler system in the mall will not necessarily operate and drive the smoke down. If, however, a fire actually occurs in the mall they will operate.

As they are part of the life safety features of the complex the sprinklers should conform to the requirements listed in Chapter 1.

5 Automatic Fire Detectors

It is recommended that all vents, extract fans and non-permanent screens should operate automatically and be activated by smoke detectors. It will, however, require very precise planning to ensure that the sequence of activation is right and one system does not nullify another (see also Chapter 19 Section 8b).

6 Conclusion

This subject is of considerable significance and interest to firefighters. It is dealt with in some detail in the Building Research Establishment report entitled 'Smoke control methods in enclosed shopping complexes of one or more storeys' dated 1979. A British Standard No. 5588 Part 10, is in preparation and is even more comprehensive but does not pretend to be the last word.

Each of these shopping developments is unique and firefighters are advised to study those in their area. The large number of people congregated in these complexes present a very high life risk and require a high standard of protective planning.

Chapter 21
Ventilation in Multi-storey Buildings

Automatic fire venting as described in the previous chapter is not generally applicable to multi-storey buildings. Although it is possible to treat the top storey as though it were a single-storey and install automatic roof vents, they would have limited application – perhaps to vent smoke from lift shafts in a fire situation.

However the use of health venting and air-conditioning systems in multi-storey buildings is increasing. The complexity of any system will, of course, be according to the building structure, number of employees, work processes being carried on etc. In all cases, such systems can present a hazard rather than a help in an outbreak of fire.

Fire prevention measures have therefore been devised to control the potential fire hazard of these systems. Such measures are designed to fulfil a similar purpose in multi-storey buildings as automatic roof vents achieve in single-storey buildings. That is:

(i)   to prevent the spread of fire, heat and smoke;

(ii)   to facilitate fire-fighting;

(iii)   to reduce damage.

In the case of multi-storey buildings they fulfil a further important function:

(iv)   to keep means of escape smoke and fire free.

1   Systems used

As described in the Manual, Book 8, mechanical ventilation systems may be divided into three main groups; those in which:

(i)   stale air is extracted by fans (fresh air finding its way in through windows and doors) – known as 'exhaust' ventilation;

(ii)   fresh air is forced in by fans (stale air finding its way out through windows and doors) – known as 'plenum' ventilation;

(iii)   fans are used to force in fresh air and extract stale air. This is a combination of (i) and (ii) and is known as 'balanced' ventilation.

Air conditioning is simply an extension of (iii) incorporating means for warming or cooling the air, providing the right humidity and so on – in fact creating an artificial environment within a building. If such a system is to be effective and economic the building has to be 'sealed' from the outside environment, thus offering little, if any, facility for natural ventilation.

All insulations have at least one plant room normally on the roof or in the basement. Large buildings may have many plant rooms, located throughout the premises but supervised from a permanently manned central control room, but readily accessible to fire service personnel responding to an incident.

2   Plant Room

A plant room should be enclosed with walls or partitions having the required standard of fire resistance.

In the case of air-conditioning plant, oil or gas may be used to warm the air, freon or other refrigerants used to cool it. These substances present a hazard in themselves and as a precaution the British Standard Code of Practice 3, Chapter IV, recommends the installation of a fire detection system which would automatically close down the plant in a fire situation.

Another relevant component of ventilation systems from the fire hazard viewpoint are air filters. Normally situated in the plant room their function is to reduce the dust content of incoming air. There are three main types of filter used:

(i)   Dry filter;

(ii)   Viscous filter;

(iii) Electrostatic filter.

(1)   Dry filter

In this filter, cotton wool, cloth or other fibrous material is used as the filtering medium. The material should, as far as possible, be flame resistant. Any accumulation of dust or dirt on the filter will greatly increase its flammability, so regular replacement is necessary, the used filter being disposed of safely.

(2)   Viscous filter

The viscous filter uses an oil-coated material to trap the dust particles in the incoming air. The oil used should have a high flash point – not less than 177°C is recommended. As with the dry filter regular maintenance is necessary. Some means of containing any surplus oil should also be provided so that it is not carried into the system.

(3)   Electrostatic filter

The important aspect of this filter from a fire point of view is that it operates at high voltages. It is therefore desirable that some means is available (either manual or automatic) to halt its operation in the event of fire. In many instances it will cease operation when the plant itself is shut down.

Where it is considered there is a high fire risk from filters, or expensive machinery needs protecting, it is possible to fit an automatic extinguishing system (e.g. sprinklers) inside the ducting, close to the filter. Such systems are normally activated by a smoke detector or fusible link (see Chapter 11 Section 2(c)).

3   The Ducting

A system of ducting for distributing, recycling and/or extracting the air, links the plant room with the rest of the building. Steel ducting is generally used (see Plate 24); if other materials are chosen they should be such so as not to substantially increase the risk of fire spread – (the British Standard Code of Practice 3, Chapter IV, Parts 2 and 3 require that the material be non-combustible and should not readily collapse when subjected to heat).

The layout of ducts in a basic air-conditioning system is shown in Fig. 21.1. In the system illustrated the branch ducts are fitted on a traditional horizontal basis.

Some systems use a modification of this arrangement as shown in Fig. 21.2. Here the branch ducts rise vertically before entering the common main duct. Structurally this arrangement is more compact and is less likely to allow a carry over of smoke in the event of fire. While smoke will rise or spread horizontally it is not so likely to descend the branch ducts.

Whatever arrangements is used however, it is the ducting which is most likely to provide the fire hazard, not only by feeding a fire with fresh air but also in the following ways:

(a)   Insulating material either inside or outside the ducts may be combustible;

(b)   Flexible joints or connections may collapse;

(c)   Smoke, heat or flame may spread through the ducting.

Fire protection measures are therefore obviously necessary in these areas.

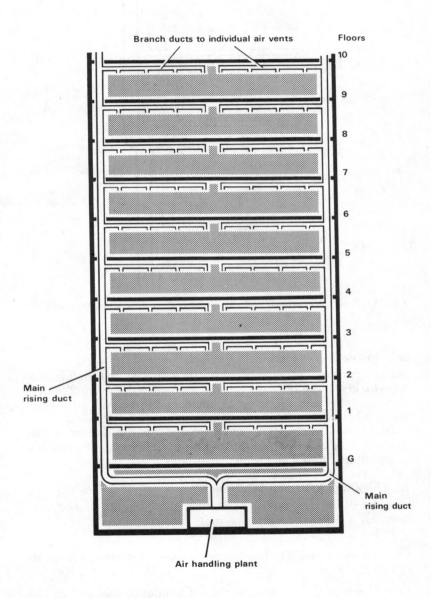

Fig. 21.1 Diagram of a basic air-conditioning system.

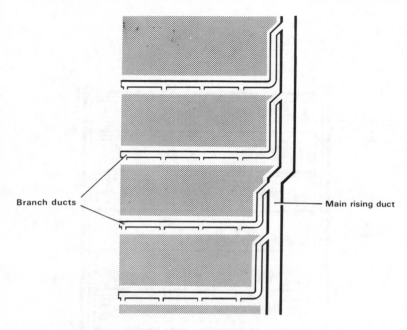

Branch ducts

Main rising duct

Fig. 21.2 A ducting system (sometimes referred to as a 'shunt' system).

a. Insulating material

From a fire prevention viewpoint it is desirable that the material used for insulating and lagging ventilation ducts should be of limited combustibility generating a minimum of smoke and toxic gases when involved in a fire.

In addition to the above requirements it is recommended that external insulating material should not be carried through fire compartment floors and walls.

b. Flexible Joints and Connections

Because of the rigid nature of ducting, flexible joints and connections are used at certain points in its construction.

In brief:

(1) 'Joints' are used to connect up sections of ductwork along its run.

(2) 'Connections' are used at the extremities to join up items of equipment (e.g. air intakes).

A feature of fires involving ventilation systems has been the collapse and destruction of these flexible joints and connections.

(1) Flexible Joints

As a general rule these are used in the main duct(s) to allow for the contraction and expansion of the metal due to normal temperature changes. They can also prevent vibrations (from the plant for example (Fig. 21.3) being transmitted through the complete system.

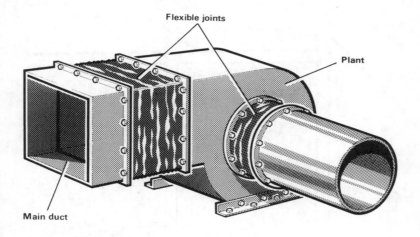

Fig. 21.3 Illustration of a flexible joint.

The collapse of a flexible joint is potentially very dangerous because this would allow fire to penetrate the main ductwork and spread throughout the building. To overcome this potential hazard there are three main recommendations in relation to installing flexible joints:

(i)   As far as practicable they should be avoided.

(ii)   they should not exceed 250mm in length;

(iii)   they should be constructed of material which gives the minimum assistance to flame spread (i.e. Class 1 BS 476, Part 7) and which does not give off excessive quantities of smoke when burnt;

(iv)   they should consist of, or be protected by, materials so as to have a fire penetration time of at least 15 minutes in accordance with BS 476.

(2)   Flexible Connections

As shown in Fig. 21.4 these are used to connect ductwork to air intake or ventilation grilles and generally to facilitate the site erection of fans, intake filters etc.

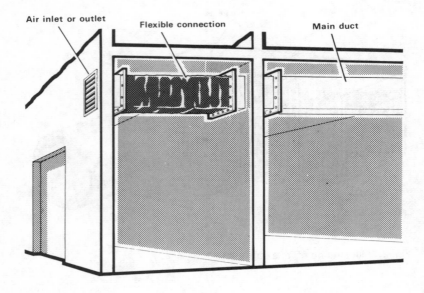

Fig. 21.4 Illustration of a flexible connection.

Because of their situation at entry or exit points to the system, flexible connections do not present quite the same potential hazard. Should a fire occur in the area of a flexible connection it could enter the system via the plant (ventilation grille, fans etc.) irrespective of whether the connections collapsed or not. Nevertheless there are certain recommendations on the use of flexible connections. These are explained in Fig. 21.5.

In addition to these three points it is important that the material used in the manufacture of flexible connections should fulfil the conditions laid down for insulating material referred to in section 3(a).

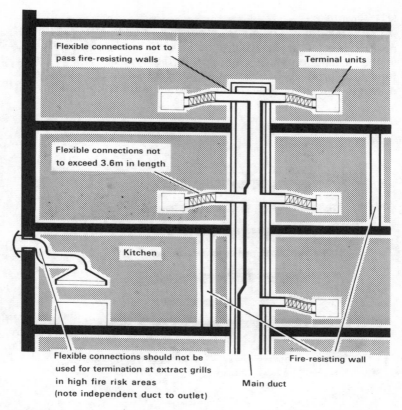

Fig. 21.5 A diagrammatic explanation of certain recommendations on the use of flexible connections.

c. Smoke, heat or flame spread through ducting

If the measures already described are implemented they will go a long way towards reducing the fire hazard of ventilation and air conditioning ducts. Nevertheless the possibility of smoke, heat or flame spread through the building (via the ducting) still remains. Combustion products may not only enter the system from within the building but, if air intakes are not thoughtfully sited on exterior walls, smoke, heat or flame may also be drawn in from outside the building.

There are three ways in which this problem can be dealt with:

(1) Proper siting of air intakes

(2) Use of fire dampers in the ducts

(3) Fire stopping of shafts carrying ducts.

(1) Air intakes

As an intake draws its air from outside a building (Fig. 21.6) its position in relation to possible exterior risks needs to be considered at the installation stage. Apart from the ordinary risk of traffic fumes the products of a fire in an adjacent building could also be drawn in and siting should aim for a minimum risk position.

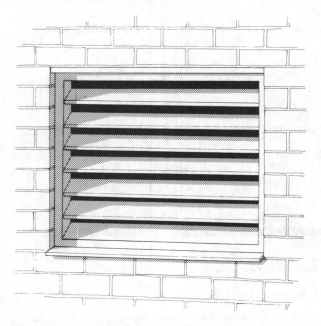

Fig. 21.6 Illustration of an air intake.

Further protection can be obtained by fixing some form of automatic closing mechanism (e.g. fire doors or dampers) to the intake. This mechanism can be made to operate by a smoke or heat sensing device depending on the nature of the exterior risk.

Regular cleaning of any wire mesh grilles covering air intakes is a necessary precaution to avoid the accumulation of combustible material such as litter and dust at the system's entry point.

(2) Fire Dampers

If air-conditioning and ventilation ducts pierce a fire-resisting compartment the resistance of the compartment is obviously reduced – smoke and fire have a ready means of access. Where it is necessary or desirable to maintain the integrity of a compartment, fire dampers can be fitted in the ducting (Fig. 21.7).

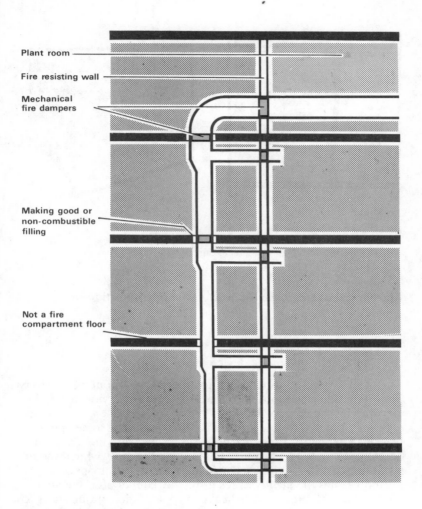

Fig. 21.7 Diagram of the use of fire dampers (in unencased ductwork).

(a) *Mechanical*

The mechanical damper in Fig. 21.8 consists of a hinged steel plate set in a steel frame. The metal used needs to be sufficiently heavy to prevent possible distortion due to heat. It should also be suitably treated to prevent corrosion in the environment in which it is to be used.

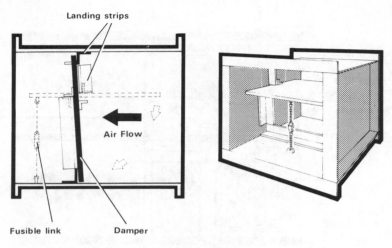

Fig. 21.8 Illustration of a mechanical damper.

Mechanical dampers can be held in the open position by:

(i)   A fusible link

or

(ii)   an electro-magnetic device (a solenoid).

The fusible link is usually set to operate at about 68°C. It is important that it is exposed to the air stream and is not shielded in any way by the damper blade.

Several types of fusible link can be fitted including some operated by smoke detectors. One such link uses an electrical impulse from a detector to initiate chemical heating of the link which should separate approximately 7 seconds after the detector operates.

Another has the facility of resetting the damper after the heat of the fire has operated it. A helical coil compression spring starts to expand at 40°C and becomes open coiled at 72°C closing the damper fully. When the temperature decreases the spring recoils opening the damper again.

An electro-magnetic device is also normally operated by a smoke detector, which can be arranged to operate either all the dampers in a system or just a particular damper (or dampers). It is important where smoke detectors are used that they are installed in positions in which they are likely to give the quickest response. In many instances this may mean installing them in a room or other part of the building rather than in the ducting itself.

On operation of the detector, or fusible link, the damper closes automatically. When closed it should fit closely against its landing strip or seating, allowing sufficient clearance for possible expansion.

Other types of mechanical damper which work on the basic principle described above are shown in Figs. 21.9(1) and (2).

Mechanical dampers fitted in a vertical position are usually gravity closed; where they are fitted in a horizontal position they can be closed by gravity, electro-magnetism or pneumatically.

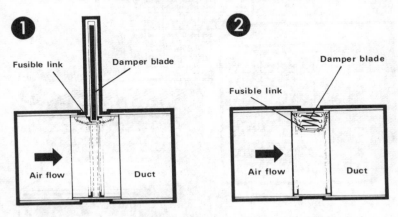

Fig. 21.9 (1) Sliding mechanical damper. (2) Shutter type mechanical damper.

(b) *Intumescent*

Another development is the intumescent coated honeycomb damper. These are fixed into the ducting as shown in Fig. 21.10. When the system is in a normal condition the damper allows free passage of air through the duct.

On heating, however, the instumescent paint will expand to approximately 100 times its original volume and form a solid mass thus preventing the passage of smoke through the duct.

The intumescence of the paint is not affected by fluff or oil spray. It should however be kept free from greasy dirt and condensation or wetness which will interfere with its effectiveness.

Intumescent honeycomb dampers are more likely to be used in duct sections where the air velocity is low (e.g. at the outlet of ventilation ducts to rooms or compartments).

There are two reasons for this:

(i)   The lower the velocity of the air in the vicinity of the damper, the smaller the loss of head in the air flow. (It should be remembered that the intumescent damper is permanently in the air flow – in the normal state, metal dampers are not in the flow to any appreciable extent.

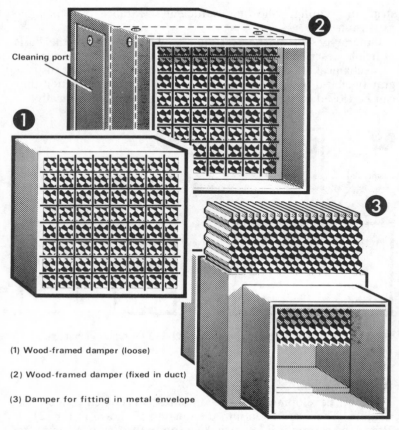

Cleaning port

(1) Wood-framed damper (loose)

(2) Wood-framed damper (fixed in duct)

(3) Damper for fitting in metal envelope

Fig. 21.10 Intumescent -coated honeycomb dampers. (1) Wood framed damper (loose). (2) Wood framed damper (fixed in the duct). (3) Damper for fitting into a metal envelope.

(ii)　If placed in the path of high velocity air the melting paint may be sucked towards the unexposed face of the damper due to the pressure difference on either side. This can obviously reduce its effectiveness.

Additional support for the honeycomb is needed if it is fixed in a horizontal position (Fig. 21.11). This is to prevent sagging of the honeycomb when the paint begins to melt in a fire condition.

Intumescent dampers will provide 40 minutes to 1 hour fire resistance depending on their thickness. Single metal dampers will normally provide up to 2 hours fire resistance. For higher standards double dampers can be used if a single damper of the required standard is not available.

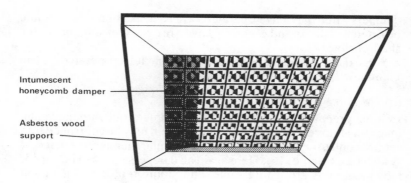

Intumescent
honeycomb damper

Asbestos wood
support

Fig. 21.11 A honeycomb damper fitted in the horizontal position.

(c) *Inspection*

Regular inspection of dampers is necessary. Particularly so with the mechanical kind. They may remain inactive for many years and the pivots, landing strips etc., can accumulate dust or dirt which would prevent, or delay, operation of the damper.

Inspection doors (Fig. 21.12) must therefore be provided in the duct adjacent to each damper. This allows not only for inspection of dampers but also for replacement of fusible links or intumescent

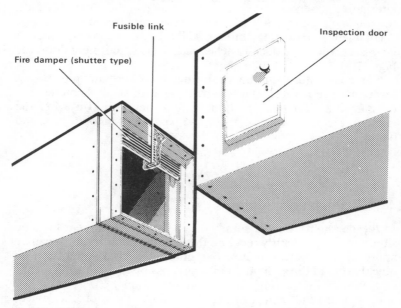

Fusible link

Inspection door

Fire damper (shutter type)

Fig. 21.12 Diagram of duct showing an inspection door adjacent to the fire damper.

191

dampers after they have operated. These inspection doors should be fitted with locks and generally have a fire resistance similar to the shaft enclosure.

Some dampers will have an indication that it has operated e.g. an illuminated LED or mechanical flag.

(d) *Multiple controls*

In some premises there may be a large number of dampers, vents, operating louvres etc., and the whole system may be controlled by a central control and indicator panel in a similar manner to a detector system (see Chapter 16). Here again all dampers etc., can be zoned, individual units are 'addressable' and monitored, the control will indicate visually and audibly any faults or actuations, inform an RMC if necessary, and either individual units or zones can be operated or tested.

(3) Fire Stopping of Shafts (encased ducting)

Where ducts are encased in shafts the possibility exists of smoke, heat or flame spread through the shaft itself. To avoid this, non-combustible infilling should normally be inserted around the duct where it breaches each fire compartment floor, so that a permanent seal is provided. If, however the duct is enclosed in a shaft with fire-resisting walls, a solid non-combustible filling need only be provided at about every 10 metres (Fig. 21.13(1)). As an alternative, a permanent vent can be created at the top of the shaft; the solid non-combustible filling is not then required (Fig. 21.13(2).

(In unencased ducting, infilling AND the provision of dampers is necessary where the duct breaches each fire compartment floor, see Fig. 21.7).

Non-combustible infilling is also needed where any pipe passes through a fire-resisting duct-shaft. Pipes with small diameters are recommended for this situation; should they perish in a fire the minimum gap is thereby left for the passage of smoke, heat and flame.

4 Recirculation Systems

In these systems a given supply of air (up to 75 per cent in some situations) is constantly recycled through the plant room. It can be appreciated therefore that smoke entering such a system can be quickly spread throughout a building, possibly jeopardising means of escape and hindering fire fighting operations.

Except in small plants or small buildings, therefore, a device, normally a smoke detector, should be installed in the extract ducting before the point where the air is separated. In the event of

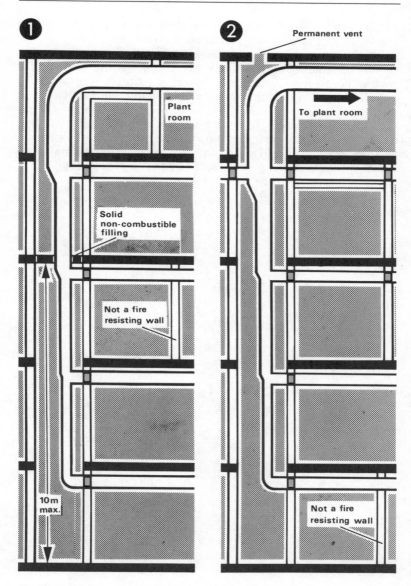

Fig. 21.13 (1) A duct shaft with non-conbustible fillings. (2) A duct shaft with a roof vent.

appreciable quantities of smoke being detected in the system, the detector will cause the re-circulation of air to cease and either discharge the return air outside the building or shut down the plant automatically. Some systems have the expensive alternative of smoke extract fans in addition to the normal fans.

In either case, a device, capable of being operated by firefighters should be installed in a position agreed by the fire authority to enable the plant to be stopped. Where practicable it may also be desirable to have a device which would enable the firefighters to start the system again should this be considered necessary to clear the building of smoke. In large buildings with a number of plant rooms these facilities may be found in the central control room (see Section 1) where firefighters can possibly seek the assistance of engineers when dealing with a technically complex system.

Chapter 22
Pressurisation

1   General

In multi-storey buildings, staircases and lobbies are a very important part of the means of escape. Once inside a 'protected route',
people in a building should be able to make their way to a final exit
and safety in the open air. Usually it is not flame but smoke and
toxic gases which will, at first, inhibit this movement. Therefore,
the exclusion of smoke and gases from 'protected routes' is very
important.

Natural ventilation relies a great deal on wind speed and direction
and the ideal conditions will not necessarily be present when a fire
starts.

Mechanical extraction systems on staircases could rapidly clear
any smoke or gases but would lower the pressure in the staircase
thus inducing a more rapid build-up of smoke from the interior of
the building.

2   Smoke movement

There are two main factors that determine the movement of smoke
arising from a fire in a building.

(a)   the greater mobility of the smoke because it consists of heated
      gases less dense than the surrounding air,

(b)   the normal air movement that can carry smoke, slowly or
      quickly, to all parts of the building.

3   Air movement

Air movement is itself governed by:

(a)   the 'stack effect' i.e. the pressure differential caused by the air
      inside the building being at a temperature different to that of
      the air outside. When there are openings, top and bottom, this
      will promote natural air-flow through the buildings; upwards
      when the building air is warmer than the outside air;
      downwards when it is cooler.

(b) The wind, because all buildings have some air leaks and wind action contributes to air movement through these leaks;

(c) any mechanical ventilation system installed in the building.

4 Pressurisation

Pressurisation provides a pressure difference which opposes, and overcomes, those generated by the factors which cause the movement of smoke. It injects air into the protected escape routes i.e. staircases, lobbies or corridors, which raises the pressure slightly above that of adjacent parts of the building. This prevents smoke and toxic gases from finding their way into the protected routes. A pressurisation system can be single or two-stage and used:

(a) only in the event of a fire (either on automatic or manual operation);

(b) on full operation whenever the building is occupied; or

(c) at reduced capacity at normal times when the building is occupied with automatic boost to full operation in the event of fire.

The nature of the building and its occupancy and economics will dictate the system chosen.

5 Requirements of a pressurisation system

The two basic considerations when designing a pressurisation system are:

(a) the pressure required in the staircase, lobby or corridor;

(b) the leakage paths

a. Pressure required

A pressurisation system, to be effective, must achieve a higher pressure than those developed by weather and fire conditions. The recommended level of pressurisation, for this country, is about 5mm water-gauge (Wg.). This represents approximately ten times the pressure normally developed in a fire and is four times the maximum pressure likely to be caused by adverse weather conditions. The air flow required to achieve this pressure is independent of the volume of space to be pressurised. In deciding on the air-flow required it is necessary to take the leakage paths into account.

b. Leakage paths

Leakage paths are, generally, those minor gaps around doors and windows which allow air to escape and they are a necessary part of a pressurisation scheme. Unless air is able to escape, the whole building will become pressurised and the necessary pressure differential (i.e. between the fire area and the protected route) will cease to exist. Leakage paths can be discussed in two stages:

(i)   initial leakage path;

(ii)   final leakage path

(i)   Initial leakage path

In most cases this will be past gaps around doors leading to individual rooms off the pressurised area or through lift doors (Fig. 22.1). It is obvious that badly fitting doors will create too large a leakage path and can unbalance a system; the maximum recommended gap is 3mm. However, in general, doors enclosing a pressurised space will also need to be fire resistant which should ensure a door that is close-fitting to the frame.

In a fire situation, of course, people will have to exit through such doors. The momentary opening of doors does not seriously affect the pressurisation system and any pressure loss is quickly reocvered when the doors close again. Obviously, doors propped open permanently will weaken the system.

A pressure of 5mm wg will mean that a little extra pressure will be required to open a door leading to the pressurised area. This is sufficiently small to allow most people to open such doors with only slightly increased effort. However, any recommendation for the design of a pressurisation system should bear this fact in mind where children or the disabled are liable to be present.

(ii)   The final leakage path

As illustrated in Fig. 22.1 this is usually through gaps in openable windows and through external doors and there will, generally, be sufficient leakage through these for the system to work. Where windows systems are sealed, as often happens in modern buildings alterntive leakage paths are usually necessary. These can be in the form of one or more of the following:

(a) Vents in external walls which open only on the operation of the pressurisation system.

(b) Natural ventilation using a vertical shaft with openings from each floor and an opening at the top. These are opened on the operation of the pressurisation system.

(c) Mechanical extraction systems. These have to be very carefully designed so as not to nullify the pressurisation system.

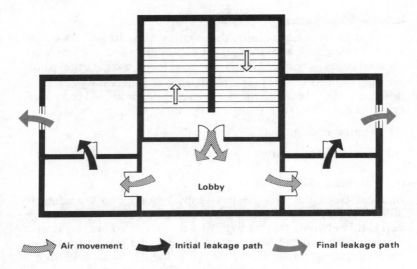

Fig. 22.1 Illustration of leakage parts.

6 Firefighting

A pressurised staircase obviously holds many advantages from a firefighting point of view, enabling firefighters to approach the area on fire through relatively clear air. It must be borne in mind however that:–

(a) the route will be used by people escaping from the building and their movement must not be impeded.

(b) in order to attack the fire, hose will have to be passed through doors which will, therefore, be held open. The extent to which this is necessary will depend on the type and height of the building. If, of course, a dry or wet riser is fitted the outlet will probably be in the lobby approach from the staircase. This will enable firefighting to take place without smoke-logging the staircase.

In other cases the officer-in-charge may have to decide to ensure evacuation of the occupants down the protected staircase before commencing firefighting.

(c) Although firefighters will, initially, approach the fire area in relatively clear air the possibilities of the staircase subsequently becoming smoked-logged because of doors being held open should be taken into account when assessing the necessity for BA.

(d) Where to position BA controls would probably need some pre-planning

Pre-knowledge of the building and how the pressurisation system works will enable the officer-in-charge to formulate a flexible approach to the problem.

7 Advice and further information

British Standard 5588 Part 4 entitled 'Code of Practice for smoke control in protected escape routes using pressurisation' gives a great deal of detail about pressurisation systems, and recommendations for designers who intend using these systems in buildings.

(This Standard uses Pascals as its measure of pressure but firefighters should know that 5mm water gauge is equal to about 50 Pascals.)

Index

Structure and publishing history of
Manual of Firemanship

The *Manual of Firemanship* was first published in a series of nine 'Parts' (1–5, 6a, 6b, 6c and 7) between 1943 and 1962.

In July 1974, it was decided that these nine Parts should be gradually replaced by 18 'Books' and a revised format for the *Manual* was drawn up. The new Books were to up-date the information given and arrange the subjects covered in more compact and coherent groups, each group occupying one of the new Books. The following pages show the original plan, *as amended to date*. Twelve of these Books have so far been published; the present volume is the second edition of Book 9.

Since 1974 there have been many developments in Fire Brigade practice and equipment and in the problems which firefighters may have to face. To remain an authoritative and up-to-date survey of the science of firefighting the *Manual* must take these developments into account. Not all the necessary changes can be accommodated within the format announced in 1974. The reader should therefore be aware that the structure of unpublished Books of the Manual, as set out on the following pages, is subject to change. Such changes with be publicised as far in advance as possible.

The next Book planned for publication is the second edition of Book 8, 'Building construction and structural fire protection' This will appear in a slightly different form and include a Part on 'Internal fire loading'.

Manual of Firemanship

Book 1 Elements of combustion and
       extinction (published in 1974)

Part	Formerly	
	Part	*Chapter*
1 Physics of combustion	*1*	*1*
2 Chemistry of combustion	*1*	*1*
3 Methods of extinguishing fire	*1 and*	*2*
	6a	*32*(III)

Book 2 Fire Brigade equipment (published
       in 1974)

Part	Formerly	
	Part	*Chapter*
1 Hose	*1*	*4*
2 Hose fittings	*1*	*5*
3 Ropes and lines, knots, slings, etc.	*1 and*	*7*
	6a	*39*
4 Small gear	*1*	*13*

Book 3 (second edition) Hand pumps,
       extinguishers and foam equipment
       (published in 1988)

Part	Formerly	
	Part	*Chapter*
1 Hand-operated pumps	*1*	*8*
2 Portable fire extinguishers and fire blankets	*1*	*9*
3 Foam and foam-making equipment	*1*	*10*

Book 4 Incidents involving aircraft,
       shipping and railways (published in
       1985)

Part	Formerly	
	Part	*Chapter*
1 Incidents involving aircraft	*6b*	*4*
2 Incidents involving shipping	*7*	*1–3*
3 Incidents involving railways	*6b*	*3*

Book 5 Ladders and appliances (published
       in 1984)

Part	Formerly	
	Part	*Chapter*
1 Extension ladders, hook ladders and roof ladders	*1*	*6*
2 Escapes	*2*	*3*
3 Turntable ladders	*2*	*4*
4 Hydraulic platforms	*2*	*5*
5 Special appliances	*2*	*6*
6 Pumping appliances	*2*	*1*

Book 6 (second edition) Breathing apparatus and resuscitation (published in 1989)

Part	Formerly Part	Chapter
1 Breathing apparatus	1	11
2 Operation procedure	6a	32(V)
3 Protective clothing	–	–
4 Resuscitation	1	12

Book 7 (second edition) Hydraulics, pumps and pump operation (published in 1986)

Part	Formerly Part	Chapter
1 Hydraulics	3	19
2 Water supplies and hydrants	3	20
3 Pumps and pump operation	2	1–2
4 Water carrying and relaying	3	21
Appendices		

Book 8 Building constructions and structural fire protection (published in 1975)

Part	Formerly Part	Chapter
1 Materials	4	23
2 Elements of structure	4	23
3 Building design	4	23

Book 9 Fire protection of buildings (published in 1990)

Part	Formerly Part	Chapter
1 Fire extinguishing systems	4	24/26
2 Fire alarm systems	5	28
3 Fire venting systems	4	23

Book 10 Fire Brigade communications (published in 1978)

Part	Formerly Part	Chapter
1 The public telephone system and its relationship to the Fire Service	5	27
2 Mobilising arrangements	5	29
3 Call-out and remote control systems	5	30
4 Radio	5	31
5 Automatic fire alarm signalling systems	5	28

Book 11 Practical firemanship I (published in 1981)

Part	Formerly Part	Chapter
1 Practical firefighting	6a	32
2 Methods of entry into buildings	6a	35
3 Control at a fire	6a	33

Book 12 Practical firemanship II (published in 1983)

Part	Formerly Part	Chapter
1 Fire Service rescues	6a	36
2 Decontamination	–	–
3 Ventilation of fires	6a	37
4 Salvage	6a	38
5 After the incident	6a	34

Book 13
Contents not yet decided

Book 14 Special fires I (not yet published)

Part	Information available in Part	Chapter	Last edition
1 Fires in animal and vegetable oils	6c	45(8)	1970
2 Fires in fats and waxes	6c	45(3)	1970
3 Fires in resins and gums	6c	45(13)	1970
4 Fires in grain, hops, etc	6c	45(6)	1970
5 Fires in fibrous materials	6c	45(4)	1970
6 Fires in sugar	6c	45(15)	1970
7 Fires in paint and varnishes	6c	45(9)	1970

Book 14 Special fires II (not yet published)

Part	Information available in Part	Chapter	Last edition
1 Fires in dust	6c	45(1)	1970
2 Fires in explosives	6c	45(2)	1970
3 Fires in metals	6c	45(7)	1970
4 Fires in plastics	6c	45(10)	1970
5 Fires involving radioactive materials	6c and	45(11)	1970
	6a	33(VI)	1871
6 Fires in refrigeration plant	6c	45(12)	1970
7 Fires in rubber	6c	45(14)	1970

Book 16 Special fires I (not yet published)

Part	Information available in Part	Chapter	Last edition
1 Fires in rural areas	6b	1	1973
2 Fires in electricity undertakings	6b	3	1973

Book 17 Special fires IV (not yet published)

Part	Information available in Part	Chapter	Last edition
1 Fires in fuels	6c	45(5)	1970
2 Fires in oil refineries	6b	5	1973
3 Fires in gas works	6b	2	1973

Book 18 Contents not yet decided

Printed in the United Kingdom for HMSO
Dd 292876 7/90 C150 488 12521